The Daniel Fast:

how to combine prayer and fasting for a wonderful spiritual and physical experience | a 21-day commitment to strenghten your spirit and renew your body.

TABLE OF CONTENTS

INTRODUCTION

Daniel is a prophet who lived in the 6th century BC and was favored by King Nebuchadnezzar. He is also known as "Danny" or "Danny South." At the end of his life, he saw a vision in which he was told that God would restore health to those living in Jerusalem if they would turn from their sins.

What is Daniel Fasting?

Daniel fasting is an eating pattern where you eat no animal products, or anything that was cooked with animal fats. You can also follow a vegan diet and still be on a Daniel Fast.

The purpose of the Daniel Fast is to help us cleanse our lives from things that might be affecting our health, such as poor food choices, stress or sleep deprivation.

Daniel fasting is done for a set period of time and then you can eat normally again. Some people choose to fast for just one full day while others do it for several weeks or even months at a time.

You need to prepare both spiritually and in a practical sense to make the most of your Daniel fast.

Here are some pointers:

- Find a spiritual purpose

First, you need to decide on a purpose for your fast. What are you seeking from God? Do you need strength or wisdom, or a revelation about a certain aspect of your life?

You should also establish a purpose based on someone else's needs, so you can pray that they find strength, wisdom or guidance. Is there someone close to you who is lost or struggling? You can pray on their behalf during your Daniel fast. Tell that person you will be praying for them during the fast.

- Prepare your pantry

It is easier to stick with an eating plan if you have all the necessary foods on hand. Stock up on whole grains,
brown rice, nuts and other important components of the fast. Plan your schedule so you are prepared to replenish your supplies of fresh fruits and vegetables every few days.

Think ahead about how you will handle social occasions, such as dinner with friends, or even lunch at work.
Planning will prevent you finding yourself hungry with nothing appropriate to eat.

Plan a few balanced meals and snacks so you're eating plan is completely ready to go!

- Know your weaknesses

If caffeine, processed foods or sweet treats are a regular part of your daily eating plan, you will find it difficult to go "cold turkey" for the duration of your fast. Your spiritual journey may be distracted by your unhealthy cravings and mood swings.

You can circumvent this by gradually cutting down on your food dependencies in the weeks leading up to the fast: consume the forbidden items less often until you can comfortably go a full day without coffee or chocolate. This way, the Daniel Fast will be an extension of your healthy eating goals rather than an impossibly strict challenge.

- See your doctor

Whenever you prepare to make drastic changes to your eating plan, make sure your doctor does a few routine tests first. Have a blood test to check your vitamin and mineral count, and ask your doctor to check your blood pressure and your glucose levels. If any of these are outside the normal range, a change in diet could aggravate the issue. For example, if your iron or Vitamin B12 levels are already low, you will become extremely lethargic when you cut meat and dairy from your daily eating plan. However, if you have all these issues checked in advance, you can tailor your diet to work around any problems.

Another benefit to seeing your doctor first is that you can take a snapshot of your health before the Daniel Fast, and then see how your health has improved after the 21-day abstinence from caffeine, sugar and processed foods.

In this book, you will find recipes, 21 days devotion of Daniel, and 21 days meal plan that not only will help you become healthier but also closer to God. Many people who have tried this eating pattern have experienced many benefits, such as weight loss, clearer skin and a great sense of well-being.

Shall we start?

FASTING

When I first learned to drive, we didn't have smartphones and apps. Maybe you have this same memory. If we needed directions, we had to unfold a giant paper map to trace the route. When going to visit someone for the first time, we would write down step-by-step instructions. We had to pay attention and remember to turn right by the school, go past the blue house with the orange fence, and stay on the lookout for other turns and landmarks.

Now, we can plug an address into our phone and mindlessly follow directions without worrying how many steps are required along the way. If we take a wrong turn, a reassuring robotic voice immediately corrects us with the notice: "recalculating route, make a U-turn."

Our technology isn't necessarily foolproof, however. Many times, I have been so deadlocked on obeying the voice in my phone that I ignored my intuition and turned left when I knew I should continue straight. Because I didn't take a few minutes on the front end to look through the entire route, I got sidetracked, and it ultimately took more time, effort, and stress to get where I was trying to go.

When it comes to fasting, we're often in the same boat (or car). We've decided to do a Daniel Fast and immediately jump to search for recipes. But that is like mindlessly following the automatic directions. We first need to survey what fasting entails from start to finish, not just for our particular plan but also for how fasting fits into the larger scope of the Bible. Although anecdotes and supplemental information can be helpful, nothing compares to searching the original source and examining what the Word of God says about fasting.

Old Testament Fasting

In the Old Testament, we see stories of people fasting in times of national crisis, while mourning, for repentance, and while seeking God. These fasts range from Daniel avoiding meat and wine to complete fasts of no food or water. We can see how God provided direction, protection, and comfort when people in need were seeking His will through prayer and fasting.

- Battle and national crisis

An early mention of fasting is found in the book of Judges. The context is battle. In this unfortunate situation, the sons of Israel went to war against the tribe of Benjamin because of an unpardonable murder that demanded justice.

During the battle, the soldiers of Israel came to the Lord with weeping and offerings, "and thus they remained before the Lord and fasted that day until evening." (Judge 20:2) When they asked the Lord whether they should continue, He told them to go. He instructed the men of Israel to set up an ambush, and they were victorious. God not only gave them the assurance to press forward, He also gave a very specific strategy for how to fight and win this battle.

In another incident, the Ammonites and Moabites threatened the kingdom of Judah. Facing an immense threat, with multitudes coming in from beyond the sea, King Jehoshaphat called the entire nation to unite and turn to the Lord for guidance. In 2 Chronicles 20:3, we read that Jehoshaphat was afraid, and as he turned his attention to seek the Lord, he proclaimed a fast throughout all Judah.

King Jehoshaphat fought this battle spiritually as well as physically. He gathered all the people of Judah, including babies and infants, as he called on the Lord and prayed. In this assembly, the Spirit of the Lord came down and one of the Levites made this great proclamation: "Do not fear or be dismayed because of this great multitude, for the battle is not yours but God's." (2 Chronicles 20:15)

Along with prayer and fasting, they also engaged in worship. As Judah marched into battle King Jehoshaphat (2 Chronicles 20:21) As this battle concluded, Judah's enemies were destroyed and the spoil was more than they could carry away.

Queen Esther is another leader who called for fasting in a time of crisis. While the Jews were in exile under the Persian Empire, Esther learned of a plot to destroy all Jews. Being a Jew herself, the only possibility of survival required Esther to go into the king to plead the case of the Jewish people . . . without being summoned. To approach the king unsummoned was a move punishable by death. But in this crisis, she had no alternative and no time to waste.

Esther called all the Jews in Susa to not eat or drink for three days, and she and her maidens would also fast at this same time (Est 4:16). She went to King Ahasuerus on the third day and not only was her life spared, but she was able to save the Jewish people and see justice served.

Although we may not face physical battles and death threats, we still confront a variety of enemies in our daily lives. Whether the attack is spiritual or manifesting through people and circumstances, do you take time to pray and fast before launching into battle?

In these particular examples, the leaders had the authority to call on the masses to engage in fasting and prayer. Even if you aren't in a political position, prayer and fasting is a powerful response to a national crisis. We are all called to intercede for justice, freedom for oppressed people, and for our governing officials.

Wisdom comes when we pause and seek the Lord first before we react. Whether it's a larger national crisis or a personal battle that you're facing, it's easy to get swept up in chaos and confusion. We need the Lord's covering and protection physically and mentally. We also need divine wisdom for our offensive strategy. Consider the favor in each of the examples above when the problem was taken to the Lord first. The leaders were victorious because of divinely inspired plans and tactics.

- Mourning

In the Bible, people fasted in times of distress and mourning. Fasting was often accompanied by demonstrative weeping and putting on sackcloth and ashes. One example is when the men of Israel fasted for seven days after burying King Saul and his son Jonathan (1 Sam 31:13).

Nehemiah was devastated when he heard the news that the walls of Jerusalem had been broken down. In this time, having strong walls around a city was vital for safety and protection. His response was to sit down and weep and mourn for several days. During this time, he was fasting and praying to God, mourning over a dire situation for his people (Nehemiah 1:4). With the walls of Jerusalem broken down, the city was exposed, and people were vulnerable. After this emotional time spent seeking the Lord, Nehemiah ultimately rose up, petitioned the king for travel and supplies, and led the team who would rebuild the wall in fifty-two days.

- Repentance

In the Old Testament, people also responded with mourning and fasting when they were convicted of sin. Repentance means changing the mind. It's one action with two parts: to stop going in one direction and start moving in another. While sin leads you in a direction of increasing separation from God, repentance is the decision to turn around and move back towards Him.

When people were engaging in sin, the prophet Joel delivered a strong message from God, calling the people to announce a time of fasting. God is seeking a true heart change through fasting.

After Jonah preached to Nineveh, the people of the city called a fast and put-on sackcloth. The king did the same and issued a proclamation that no man or beast should eat or drink, but that each should turn from their wicked ways and honor God (Jon 3:8). The prophet's message pierced the hearts of the people, and they all responded.

- Seeking God

Whether faced with a threat, a tragedy, or conviction of your own sin, certain moments shake your assumption of self-sufficiency. When you're at the end of your rope with nowhere else to turn, God can step in and provide the answers you need.

In addition to the examples already listed, here are some more instances of people seeking the Lord with fasting:

1. David was struck with grief for his son who was near death. "David therefore inquired of God for the child; and David fasted and went and lay all night on the ground." (2 Sam 12:16)
2. Hannah desperately wanted a child, and wept and did not eat as she prayed and "poured out [her] soul before the Lord." (1 Sam 1:15)

3. Daniel was convicted for the sins and iniquities of his people as he read the book of Jeremiah. (Dan 9:3)
4. The Israelites needed direction when returning from exile to Jerusalem to rebuild the temple, (Ezra 8:23)

New Testament Fasting

There are significant mentions of fasting in the New Testament, starting with the birth of Jesus. A widow named Anna was in the temple when Jesus was presented as a baby. She is called a prophetess, and the gospel says she never left the temple but served around the clock with fasting and prayer. When she saw the baby, she immediately recognized that the infant Jesus was the Messiah. She gave thanks to God and continued to speak about Him to everyone in Jerusalem (Luke 2:36–38).

Although fasting was sometimes a response to anguish and mourning, here is a beautiful picture of a joyful life devoted to worship, prayer, and fasting! Embracing fasting as an act of worship and part of her spiritual rhythm, Anna was close to God and sensitive to His spirit, which enabled her to instantly recognize Jesus.

The book of Acts shows us the lives of Jesus's apostles and followers immediately following His death and ascension into heaven. The church began with people who referred to themselves as "disciples of the Lord" and followers of "the Way" (Acts 19:23). Acts 11:26 says the disciples were first called Christians at Antioch.

They united as a family, a community with common principles and values. This is the birth of the church. These believers established the first example of gathering, worshiping, and walking out their faith. Along with these other practices, fasting was a regular part of their lives.

As the leaders of the church fasted and worshiped together, the Holy Spirit instructed them to set Barnabas and Saul (Paul) apart. So, they fasted, prayed, laid hands on them, and sent them on their way (Acts 13:2–3). As they were sent out by the Holy Spirit, they were empowered in both direction and mission.

If you have a decision to make, these scriptures from the book of Acts should be especially encouraging. God wants to guide you. As Paul and Barnabas traveled (Acts 14:23)

Fasting is again used as a ministry tool and for the benefit of others. When we fast and pray, we're not just looking introspectively to improve our own condition but also looking up and out so we impact others in our sphere of influence with God's will and strategies at the forefront of our minds. As you fast, consider how you can do good to others, encourage them, and pray for them.

Supernatural encounters occurred during times of prayer and fasting. Saul (who was later called Paul) was traveling to Damascus to look for Christians, known as followers of "the Way," to imprison them.

He had an encounter with the Lord, and Jesus spoke to him and directed him to visit Ananias, a disciple who was living in Damascus. Saul fasted for three days and was unable to see.

During this same time, the Lord told Ananias in a vision that he should lay hands on Saul. Although he was apprehensive because of Saul's reputation and the preceding harm he had done, when the two men met, they had both heard from God and obeyed His supernatural direction. After Ananias laid hands-on Saul, something like scales fell from his eyes and he was able to see, and he took food and was strengthened (see Acts 9:1–19).

Another divine encounter occurs in Acts Chapter 10. Cornelius was a Roman centurion who worshiped God. As he was praying and fasting, God told him to send for Peter. Simultaneously, Peter received a vision from God that was symbolic of God's will to preach the gospel to all people, not only Jews but also Gentiles.

With this preface, when Peter was called to the house of this Roman soldier, the Spirit directed him to go. As Peter preached the gospel to this family, the Holy Spirit fell on everyone listening with power, and the entire household was saved (see Acts 10:1–48).

This is not an exhaustive list of every mention of fasting in the Bible. You can find a list of scripture references to diet, food, and fasting in the appendix, and I encourage you to take your own time in Bible study to read more.

Your Journey

These biblical examples have a key thread in common. In every circumstance, people are seeking God for His will and direction. Fasting is often a response to distress, accompanied by strong emotion and a desperation for answers. Our world would look significantly different if our first response to trouble was to turn to God with prayer and fasting instead of gravitating towards food, alcohol, technology, or other addictive substances.

Continue to pray and dive deeper into God's word for encouragement and revelation on fasting and consider what this means for your own life.

THE DANIEL FAST

What Is the Daniel Fast?

The Daniel Fast originated based on a scripture found in Daniel 1:12. And also in Daniel 10:1-2

The Daniel Fast is about only putting into the body healthy and natural foods while building a stronger relationship with the Lord. During the Fast, you can eat as much as you want, as often as you want, as long as you eat only vegetables and fruits, and drink only water – be sure to check out this guide's list of delicious recipes.

Think of the Fast as a cleansing of the body and the spirit as you deny yourself a few of your favorites, like chocolate and French fries, by learning patience and self-control.

Is the Daniel Fast for Me?

So, who can participate in the Daniel Fast? Everyone!

The Daniel Fast is designed to be a personal journey between you and the Lord, so design your individual plan and implement the Daniel Fast into your life as the next step to becoming closer with our Savior.

The Daniel Fast can be followed by individuals and families alike.

As a single person, you might feel that taking on such a commitment might be too overwhelming or time consuming. This guide, however, will give you tips to stay on the 'diet,' encouraging scriptures to read during difficult times, and plenty of recipes that you can make in advance or in a few minutes to ensure you can succeed.

A family might find it more difficult to get everyone onboard with the Daniel Fast, especially if there are children. However, getting the kids involved in planning menus, deciding on prayers and scriptures and encouraging them to help 'you' stay on track will not only make it easier, it will help to bring the family closer as you all work together for an individual and common goal. Not only will the family learn healthier eating habits and acquire healthier bodies, they will also be developing a better relationship with the Lord on an individual basis while bringing the family closer together.

What Kind of Results Can I Expect?

Although the Daniel Fast is not designed to be a weight loss program, many people find themselves losing a few pounds during the fast. Some people may experience more weight loss than others, depending upon their 'normal' diet habits.

- Your Soul and Spirit

First and foremost, you should expect to have a deeper connection with the Lord. As you concentrate on prayer and scriptures while cleansing your body, you will develop a stronger connection with the Savior. Even if you are not a believer, or if you have lost some of your faith, reading the scriptures or just taking that time to meditate will help to relieve your mind and spirit of every day stressors. Quiet time spent in conversation with the Lord, or by doing other meditating activities such as Yoga, will help you develop skills to be in control of your life, of your thoughts and of how you deal with life in general.

Taking time out from distractions such as television, social media and other things will give you more time to devote to the Lord and to yourself. It will help you to become less dependent on technology and modern distractions while you become stronger and more capable in your life's dealings. You will find it much easier to concentrate, whether at work, home or other activities and it will be easier to do with the little crisis that before seemed like such a huge ordeal.

- Your Body and Health

Every day we put processed foods and chemicals into our bodies. Most of us don't even realize just how much artificial and harmful chemicals we consume in a single day. You may not even realize that many of the foods you eat develop an addiction, and the body responds with withdrawal symptoms if it doesn't get them.

As you continue with the Daniel Fast, you'll begin to notice changes in your body. Excluding unhealthy foods and chemicals will actually add energy and focus. You may even find some of the daily aches and pains you suffer from start to ease or disappear altogether.

Committing to the Daniel Fast has also been known to help, and even "claimed" to have cured in some cases certain health problems and diseases. Ridding the body of toxins and chemicals has been known to help with asthma and allergies. Testimonies from those who have participated in the Fast have noted lower blood pressure results. Some people have even claimed that the Daniel Fast has helped them with cancer.

- Weight Loss

Again, while the Daniel Fast is not designed for weight loss, it is common for people to experience some, if not a lot, of weight loss during the 21-day Fast. This, of course, is due to cutting out too much fat, sugars, processed foods, chemicals and other foods that are not good for our bodies.

Let's take salt for example. Salt causes water retention and water retention causes weight gain. If your body does not have enough water, it will store what it has which causes the retention. Sugars, fats, processed foods and chemicals all add to weight gain, not to mention hormones that are also in non-natural foods.

Once you take these foods out of your regular diet, you will see a weight loss.

- Withdrawals

Depending on your regular diet, when you first start the Daniel Fast you will likely experience withdrawal symptoms. These symptoms can include anything from anxiety to headaches. The severity of the withdrawals will depend upon your earlier diet. However, don't despair. This guide will show you ways to get through this by prayers and scriptures as well as beforehand preparation (such as starting to cut down on certain foods before the Fast).

The withdrawals are a part of the process your body may go through as it rids itself of all of the harmful toxins it has been used to consuming. Just as with drugs, unhealthy foods will likely cause some people to go into withdrawals when they cut those foods out of their diets. But don't worry; this guide will help you to prepare in advance to make the chances of withdrawal less likely and less noticeable.

21 DAYS DEVOTIONS OF DANIEL

What is your prayer life like? What are your daily thoughts? Did you know if you write your daily thoughts down and search the Bible for the scripture(s), you can easily pray over your situation and prayers will be answered? God has made us promises, and it is okay to remind Him of His promises. I have prayed over my circumstances many times and the results are phenomenal. Even when my prayer life was not as strong as it is now, my connection with God is more vertical than horizontal. I am happy that God has placed me in a position where I can stay focus on purpose and passion that He has given to me. It may have taken some time to come to this realization, but I trust Him with my whole life and I want to stay in His will to reap the benefits of His promises.

Ask God to make your prayer life stronger as you go through the Daniel Fast. Connect with God on a deeper level by writing your thoughts and praying over them. Know that you are having a conversation with Him and He is listening. I have provided 21- Days of Daily Scriptures for meditation. As you meditate on the scriptures daily, repeat them throughout the day. Stay focus, stay positive, and know your purpose and passion. Use your pen or pencil to write your daily thoughts and speak life into your thoughts. Ask God to increase your knowledge and wisdom.

Day 1: Daily Scripture and Prayer

Thessalonians 5:18 - Pray for God's will to be done in our lives, our families and for our Church family.

My Daily Thoughts:

_____

_____

_____

Day 2 Daily Scripture and Prayer

Jeremiah 29:11 Pray for God's purposes to be accomplished in our lives.

My Daily Thoughts:

_____

_____

_____

Day 3 Daily Scripture and Prayer

Acts 5:12 - Pray for the salvation of your family, friends and colleagues.

My Daily Thoughts:

_____

_____

_____

Day 4 Daily Scripture and Prayer

Romans 12: 1-2 - Pray for God's renewal of our minds so we can be a loving church, that we may love each other, and love those that are new to our church.

My Daily Thoughts:

_____

_____

_____

Day 5 Daily Scripture and Prayer

2 Corinthians 7:1- Pray for God's forgiveness and purity to be released in our lives for our spiritual growth.

My Daily Thoughts:

_____

_____

_____

Day 6 Daily Scripture and Prayer

Luke 4:40 - Pray for healing for all those that are suffering physically, emotionally and psychologically challenged (make a list of people you know that needs prayer. Pray daily for them).

My Daily Thoughts:

_____

_____

_____

Day 7 Daily Scripture and Prayer

Philippians 4:19 - Pray for God's provision for those that have unemployed and are facing financial difficulties.

My Daily Thoughts:

_____

_____

_____

Day 8 Daily Scripture and Prayer

Ephesians 2:10 - Pray for a heart for missions, to reaches out to the lost. Help us Lord to do what you have called us to do.

My Daily Thoughts:

_____

_____

_____

Day 9 Daily Scripture and Prayer

Proverbs 21:1 - Pray for God's wisdom for our government leaders that they may lead in righteousness.

My Daily Thoughts:

_____

_____

_____

Day 10 Daily Scripture and Prayer

John 16:8-9 - Pray for God's Salvation to come to those who have yet to take the step of faith.

My Daily Thoughts:

_____

_____

_____

Day 11 Daily Scripture and Prayer

Chronicles 7:14 - Pray that God will heal our land, our city, and our economy as we seek Him in prayer.

My Daily Thoughts:

_____

_____

_____

Day 12 Daily Scripture and Prayer

Ephesians 4:11- 13 - Pray for our Pastor's and ministry leaders, and worship leaders, that they receive wisdom and knowledge as they lead our churches.

My Daily Thoughts:

_____

_____

_____

Day 13 Daily Scripture and Prayer

Romans 10: 14-15 - Pray for our marriages and family ministries. Pray for our church families Pray for families living in all states and nation.

My Daily Thoughts:

_____

_____

_____

Day 14 Daily Scripture and Prayer

Exodus 15:26 - Pray that God's word would bring salvation, deliverance, healing, reverse of chronic illnesses and diseases.

My Daily Thoughts:

_____

_____

_____

Day 15 Daily Scripture and Prayer

John 16:33 - Pray for God's Love & Peace to cover our relationships, that we may live in harmony with each other.

My Daily Thoughts:

_____

_____

_____

Day 16 Daily Scripture and Prayer

1 John, 4:1- Pray that we would share God's love with our families, neighbors, school's colleges/universities, and businesses.

My Daily Thoughts:

_____

_____

_____

Day 17 Daily Scripture and Prayer

1 Peter 4:10 - Pray for our ministry volunteers. Pray for strength, resources, provisions as they are doing God's will by serving others.

My Daily Thoughts:

_____

_____

Day 18 Daily Scripture and Prayer

Deuteronomy 10:17 -18 - Pray for God's protection for those in our church who are widows, fatherless, motherless, single mothers and fathers. Not only for our church, but for our entire universe. Pray for the homeless.

My Daily Thoughts:

_____

_____

_____

Day 19 Daily Scripture and Prayer

Matthew 9:36 -38 - Pray that God will put a greater desire on our hearts to reach the lost and broken hearted around us.

My Daily Thoughts:

_____

_____

_____

Day 20 Daily Scripture and Prayer

Micah 6:8 - Pray for our local, state, and nation government leaders, that they would seek God's help as they lead our Nation.

My Daily Thoughts:

_____

_____

_____

Day 21 Daily Scripture and Prayer

Psalms 51:14 -15 - Thank the Lord for your salvation; praise Him as we give him honor and praise for the forgiveness of our sins.

My Daily Thoughts:

_____

_____

_____

Recommended Bible app for Bible reading and audio listening: Bible Gateway

FOODS TO EAT AND TO AVOID

Daniel Fast is based on fasting experiences of Prophet Daniel as recorded in the Bible. Scriptures give us some insight into what he ate and what he did not eat; however, we do not know his complete menu. What we know is: In Daniel 1, Daniel had chosen not to eat royal food, which was being served to him and he ate only fruits and vegetables and drank water. Another time he deprived choice food, meat, and wine because he sought Lord in the prayer. Most commentaries believe "choice food" would have been sweets and bread.

This is why, I believe, we will find some variation in specific guidelines for the current Daniel Fast, so far as what foods will be included and which ones will be restricted. The food guidelines are the ones that are most commonly described in the Daniel Fast. The aim of today's Daniel Fast is not to replicate precisely what Daniel did but the spirit in which he did it. Daniel's hunger for the Lord triggered him to starve and thirst more for spiritual food than for physical food, which should be the desire of anyone choosing to participate in this type of fast.

The Daniel Fast Guidelines

The most important impression behind this fast is to replicate Daniel's spiritual hunger and grow closer to the Lord instead of replicating his menu. Therefore, we should try not to be excessively hung up on what we should eat and what should not. These guidelines are meant to be just used as a guide. They are given to help us create boundaries for our fast.

Foods to Eat:

- All fruits – fresh, frozen, juiced, dried, or canned.
- All vegetables – frozen, fresh, juiced, dried, or canned.
- All whole grains –brown rice, barley, quinoa, millet, amaranth, oats, in addition whole wheat.

- All nuts and seeds – cashews, almonds, macadamia nuts, pecans, pine nuts, peanuts, walnuts, sesame seeds, sunflower seeds and pumpkin seeds; unsweetened almond milk and Nut butters are included as well.
- All legumes – dried or canned; black beans, cannellini beans, great northern beans, garbanzo beans (chickpeas), kidney beans, pinto beans, black-eyed peas, split peas, and lentils.
- All quality oils – grapeseed, avocado, coconut, olive, sesame, peanut, and walnut.
- Beverages –distilled water, filtered water, and spring water,
- Others – unsweetened almond milk, rice milk, coconut milk, or soymilk; spices, herbs, salt, pepper, unsweetened coconut flakes, soy products, seasonings, tofu and Bragg's Liquid Aminos.

Foods to Avoid:

- All meats and animal foodstuffs –beef, buffalo, bacon, eggs, fish, poultry, lamb, and pork.
- All dairy products – butter, cream, cheese, yogurt, and milk.
- All sweeteners – agave nectar, brown rice syrup, artificial sweeteners, cane juice, molasses, honey, syrups, stevia, raw sugar and sugar.
- All leavened breads& yeast – Ezekiel bread and baked goods (containing honey and yeast).
- All refined foods & processed foods – artificial flavorings, food additives, preservatives, chemicals, white rice, and white flour.
- All deep-fried foods –French fries, corn chips, and potato chips.
- All solid fats – lard, shortening, and margarine.
- Beverages – alcohol, energy drinks, carbonated drinks, coffee, herbal tea, and tea.

How to Plan A Meal on Daniel Fast?

Daniel Fast calls for some exclusive balancing moves. It is not like a "normal fast" where we drink only water and nothing else. In addition, it is not like a "juice fast" where our choices are defined clearly.

Daniel Fast is a "partial fast", so on this diet some foods are eaten and other foods are allowed. In addition, choices are many. Therefore, we will need to spend a little time in thinking about foods and food choices for meals. However, we do not want food to become our focus and we do not want Daniel Fast to become another way for satisfying our taste desires by preparing yummy and delicious meals.

That does not mean our meals should not taste good. It does mean we want to give preference to Jesus and our growing relationship with Him on this fast and not to the food!

So how can we still eat according to the guidelines of Daniel Fast and not lose our self-control? Here are a few simple steps we can take to achieve that.

We should decide to eat simpler for this period of fasting and prayer. We should consider the purpose of the fasting and how this can be a powerful period for putting our flesh under the authority of Spirit. We should not make Daniel Fast more complicated than it requires being and should be! Humble meals, Simple dishes, Pleasing and Flavorful meals are fine, but they should be in balance for the real purpose of this fasting- to restrict the food for spiritual purpose.

We should plan a small number of simple meals, i.e., we should plan just 3 breakfast menus, 3 snacks, 4-5 lunch menus (using leftovers from the preceding dinner is great), and then 5-6 dinner menus. Then we can rotate these menus. We should make sure we have the Ingredients on hand and get good at preparing these menus. We should keep our meals undemanding and uncomplicated. Then we will not have to be so obsessive about meals preparation, instead we can focus on the God, prayer and study.

We should plan and prepare a number of meals (five to six) at a time and use the leftover time for praying, listening to devotional music, memorizing scripture or listening to spiritual teachings.

Using the simple approaches mentioned above will do two things. First, when we plan and prepare various meals ahead, we will be ready and have primary parts of our meals on hand! We will not need to worry about what to eat for dinner. We will know and it will be easy and simple for us to finish meal and stay on fast.

Second, we will not be anxious! Many people end up quitting this fast as a result of one of the two reasons: 1) they felt making all meals every day took so much energy and time; 2) these meals were so complicated and so expensive. We can avoid these issues by keeping our meals simple and making them ahead.

The important benefit about this is that we will not be centered on food. To make sure we do not miss out the blessing of the fast, we should keep our meals simple. We should plan only a small number of menus that we like and can rotate them repeatedly.

Sample Menu Plan

Breakfast:

Fruit Smoothie

Fresh Fruit Salad

Steel-cut oats

Lunch:

Raw vegetable salad flavored with Vinegar/Oil Dressing

Bowl of Legume soup

Sliced Fruit

Selection of nuts

Dinner:

Vegetable stews and soups

Brown rice

Selection of cooked vegetables or stir-fry

Veggie burger (Optional)

Quick Snacks:

Popcorn

A piece of fruit

Dried fruits

Rice cakes with nut butters

This sample meal plan holds a number of options for variety! We can change the fruits used in smoothies, vary the legumes used for making soup, and combine different vegetables in the soups and stir-fry.

BREAKFAST RECIPES

1. Delish Banana Porridge

Preparation Time: 10 Minutes
Cooking Time: 5 Minutes
Servings: 2 to 4
INGREDIENTS:
- Porridge
- 2 ripe bananas, peeled and mashed
- ¾ cup almond meal
- ¼ cup flax meal
- ½ teaspoon ground ginger
- 1 teaspoon ground cinnamon
- 1/8 teaspoon ground nutmeg
- 1/8 teaspoon ground cloves
- Salt as required
- 2 cups unsweetened coconut milk
- Toppings
- 1 medium banana, peeled and sliced
- ¼ cup fresh berries

DIRECTIONS:

1. In a pan, mix all of the ingredients over medium-low heat and bring to a gentle simmer, stirring continuously.
2. Cook for about 2–3 minutes or until desired consistency is achieved, stirring continuously.
3. Serve with a topping of banana slices and berries.

NUTRITION: Calories 533, Fat 37.7 g, Carbs 41.1 g, Sugar 20.3 g, Protein 10.5 g, Sodium 102 mg

2. Gluten-Free Breakfast Porridge

Preparation Time: 10 Minutes
Cooking Time: 20 Minutes
Servings: 4
INGREDIENTS:
- Porridge
- 1 tablespoon coconut oil
- 1 teaspoon ground ginger
- 2 teaspoons ground cinnamon
- ½ teaspoon ground cloves
- 1½ cups ground millet
- 1½ cups water
- 1-quart unsweetened coconut milk
- Toppings
- 1 large banana, peeled and sliced
- ¼ cup fresh blueberries

DIRECTIONS:
1. In a saucepan, melt the coconut oil over medium-low heat and sauté the spices for about 30 seconds.
2. Add the millet and stir to combine.
3. Stir in the water and coconut milk and bring to a boil.
4. Adjust the heat to low and simmer partially covered for about 10–15 minutes.
5. Serve with a topping of banana slices and blueberries.

NUTRITION: Calories 710, Fat 39.8 g, Carbs 70.1 g, Sugar 10.6 g, Protein 11.8 g, Sodium 80 mg

3. Healthier Morning Oatmeal

Preparation Time: 15 Minutes
Cooking Time: 3 Minutes
Servings: 4
INGREDIENTS:
- Oatmeal
- ½ tablespoon coconut oil
- 2 cups old-fashioned rolled oats
- ¼ teaspoon ground cinnamon
- ¼ teaspoon kosher salt

- 1½ cups water
- Toppings
- 2 tablespoons walnuts, chopped
- ½ cup fresh blueberries

DIRECTIONS:
1. Melt the coconut oil in a saucepan over medium heat and toast the oats for about 2–3 minutes, stirring frequently.
2. Stir in the cinnamon and salt and remove from heat.
3. Stir in the water. Cover.
4. Set aside for about 7 minutes before serving.
5. Serve with a topping of blueberries and walnuts.

NUTRITION: Calories 229, Fat 7.6 g, Carbs 35.1 g, Sugar 1.8 g, Protein 8.1 g, Sodium 148 mg

4. Perfect Baked Oatmeal

Preparation Time: 15 Minutes
Cooking Time: 50 Minutes
Servings: 6
INGREDIENTS:
- Olive oil cooking spray
- 1½ cups unsweetened almond milk
- 1½ cups old-fashioned rolled oats
- ¼ cup dates, pitted and chopped
- ¼ cup dried apricots, chopped
- ¼ cup walnuts, chopped
- ½ cup unsweetened applesauce
- ½ teaspoon ground cinnamon
- ¼ teaspoon salt

DIRECTIONS:
1. Preheat the oven to 350°F.
2. Lightly grease an 8x8-inch baking dish with cooking spray.
3. Place all of the ingredients in a bowl and mix until well combined.
4. Transfer the mixture into the prepared baking dish and spread in an even layer.
5. Bake for approximately 45–50 minutes or until the top turns golden brown.

NUTRITION: Calories 165, Fat 5.8 g, Carbs 25.8 g, Sugar 7.4 g, Protein 25.3 g, Sodium 163 mg

5. Warming Breakfast Granola

Preparation Time: 15 Minutes
Cooking Time: 3 Hours
Servings: 10
INGREDIENTS:
- Olive oil cooking spray

- ¼ cup coconut oil
- ¼ cup pineapple juice
- 1½ teaspoons vanilla extract
- ½ teaspoon ground cinnamon
- ½ teaspoon kosher salt
- ½ cup dates, pitted
- ¼ cup roasted almonds
- 3 cups rolled oats
- 1¼ cups quick-cooking oats
- ¼ cup sunflower seeds
- ½ cup dried cranberries
- ½ cup raisins

DIRECTIONS:
1. Preheat the oven to 200°F.
2. Lightly grease a baking sheet with cooking spray.
3. Place the coconut oil and pineapple juice in a microwave-safe bowl and microwave for about 1 minute.
4. Stir in the vanilla, cinnamon, and salt.
5. Place the dates, almonds, and pineapple juice mixture in a high-powered blender and pulse for about 15 seconds.
6. Transfer the date mixture to a bowl. Add the rolled oats and sunflower seeds and mix well.
7. Add the quick-cooking oats and stir gently to combine.
8. Place the mixture on the prepared baking sheet and spread it in an even layer.
9. Bake for approximately 2½ hours.
10. Stir in the cranberries and raisins.
11. Bake for approximately 30 minutes more.
12. Remove from oven and set aside to cool for about 30 minutes before serving.

NUTRITION: Calories 276, Fat 10.2 g, Carbs 41.1 g, Sugar 11.2 g, Protein 7.2 g, Sodium 95 mg

6. Unique Quinoa Bread

Preparation Time: 10 Minutes
Cooking Time: 1 Hour and 30 Minutes
Servings: 12
INGREDIENTS:
- 1¾ cups uncooked quinoa, soaked overnight and rinsed
- ¼ cup chia seeds, soaked overnight in ½ cup water
- ½ teaspoon baking soda
- Salt as required
- ¼ cup olive oil
- ½ cup water
- 1 tablespoon fresh lemon juice

DIRECTIONS:

1. Preheat the oven to 320°F.
2. Line a loaf pan with parchment paper.
3. Place all of the ingredients in a high-powered food processor and pulse for about 3 minutes.
4. Transfer the mixture to the prepared loaf pan.
5. Bake for approximately 1½ hours.
6. Remove from oven and place on a wire rack for about 10 minutes.
7. Carefully invert the bread loaf onto the wire rack to cool completely before serving.
8. Slice and serve.

NUTRITION: Calories 137, Fat 6.5 g, Carbs 16.9 g, Sugar 0 g, Protein 4 g, Sodium 20 mg

7. Weight-Loss Chia Pudding

Preparation Time: 10 Minutes
Cooking Time: 0 Minutes
Servings: 4
INGREDIENTS:

- 2/3 cup unsweetened almond milk
- 2 cups frozen blueberries
- ½ frozen banana, peeled and sliced
- 5 large soft dates, pitted and chopped
- ½ cup chia seeds
- ½ cup fresh mixed berries

DIRECTIONS:

1. Add all of the ingredients except for the chia seeds to a high-powered food processor and pulse until smooth.
2. Transfer the mixture to a bowl.
3. Add the chia seeds and mix well.
4. Refrigerate for 30 minutes, stirring every 5 minutes.
5. Top with berries and serve.

NUTRITION: Calories 159, Fat 6 g, Carbs 30.1 g, Sugar 16.8 g, Protein 4.3 g, Sodium 31 mg

8. Favorite Banana Bread

Preparation Time: 15 Minutes
Cooking Time: 40 Minutes
Servings: 12
INGREDIENTS:

- Olive oil cooking spray
- 2 tablespoons flaxseed meal
- 1/3 cup water
- 2½ cups almond flour
- ½ teaspoon ground cinnamon

- ½ teaspoon ground nutmeg
- ½ teaspoon salt
- 3 large overripe bananas, peeled and mashed
- 1/3 cup coconut oil, melted
- ½ cup pecans, chopped

DIRECTIONS:
1. Preheat the oven to 350°F.
2. Grease a 9×5-inch loaf pan with cooking spray.
3. Place the flaxseed meal and water in a mug and mix well. Set aside for about 10 minutes.
4. In a large mixing bowl, mix the almond flour, spices, and salt.
5. Add the flaxseed mixture, mashed banana, and coconut oil and mix well.
6. Gently fold in the pecans.
7. Transfer the mixture to the prepared loaf pan.
8. Bake for approximately 40 minutes.
9. Remove from oven and place on a wire rack for about 10 minutes.
10. Carefully invert the bread loaf onto the wire rack to cool completely before serving.
11. Slice and serve.

NUTRITION: Calories 271, Fat 22.8 g, Carbs 12.1 g, Sugar 4.7 g, Protein 1.1 g, Sodium 98 mg

9. Inspiring Blueberry Muffins

Preparation Time: 15 Minutes
Cooking Time: 25 Minutes
Servings: 10
INGREDIENTS:
- Olive oil cooking spray
- 1 cup oat flour
- 1 cup old-fashioned oats
- 1 teaspoon ground cinnamon
- ½ teaspoon ground cardamom
- 1 cup unsweetened applesauce
- 1/3 cup date honey
- 2 medium ripe bananas, peeled and mashed
- 1 teaspoon vanilla extract
- 11/3 cups fresh blueberries

DIRECTIONS:
1. Preheat the oven to 350°F.
2. Lightly grease 10 cups of a regular muffin tin with cooking spray.
3. In a large mixing bowl, mix the oat flour, oats, and spices.
4. In a second bowl, beat the applesauce, honey, and bananas until well combined.
5. Add the flour mixture and mix until just combined.
6. Gently fold in the blueberries.
7. Transfer the mixture into the prepared muffin cups.

8. Bake for 20–25 minutes or until a toothpick inserted in the center comes out clean.
9. Remove from oven and place on a wire rack to cool for about 10 minutes.
10. Carefully invert the muffins onto the wire rack to cool completely before serving.

NUTRITION: Calories 145, Fat 2.7 g, Carbs 32.3 g, Sugar 18 g, Protein 3.1 g, Sodium 3 mg

10. Morning-Glory Muffins

Preparation Time: 15 Minutes
Cooking Time: 30 Minutes
Servings: 6
INGREDIENTS:
- Olive oil cooking spray
- ½ large tomato, finely chopped
- 19 ounces firm tofu, pressed and drained
- ¼ cup nutritional yeast
- ½ teaspoon ground turmeric
- ½ green bell pepper, seeded and chopped finely
- 3 fresh mushrooms, finely chopped
- ¾ cup broccoli, finely chopped
- 4 scallions, finely chopped
- Pinch of salt
- Pepper as required

DIRECTIONS:
1. Preheat the oven to 375°F.
2. Grease a 12-cup muffin tin with cooking spray.
3. Place the tomato pieces on a paper towel-lined plate to remove the excess liquid.
4. Place the tofu, nutritional yeast, and turmeric in a high-powered blender and pulse until smooth and creamy.
5. Transfer the tofu mixture to a bowl.
6. Add the vegetables, salt, and pepper, and stir to combine.
7. Transfer the mixture into the prepared muffin cups.
8. Bake for 25–30 minutes or until the tops turn golden brown.
9. Remove from oven and place on a wire rack to cool for about 10 minutes.
10. Carefully invert the muffins onto a platter and serve warm.

NUTRITION: Calories 102, Fat 4.3 g, Carbs 7.8 g, Sugar 2 g, Protein 11.4 g, Sodium 49 mg

11. Hot Fruity Breakfast Cereal

Preparation Time: 15 Minutes
Cooking Time: 10 Minutes
Servings: 8
INGREDIENTS:
- 2 cups cooked brown rice

- 1 (14½-ounce) can coconut milk
- 1 cup dates, pitted and roughly chopped
- 1 banana, peeled and mashed
- 1 apple, cored and chopped
- 1½ teaspoons ground cinnamon
- Pinch of ground nutmeg
- Topping
- 2 apples, cored and sliced

DIRECTIONS:
1. Place all of the ingredients except for the apple slices in a medium saucepan and stir to combine well.
2. Place the pan over medium-low heat and cook for about 10 minutes, stirring frequently.
3. Remove from heat and divide the cereal into serving bowls.
4. Top with the apple slices and serve hot.

NUTRITION: Calories 289, Fat 12.9 g, Carbs 45.5 g, Sugar 26.3 g, Protein 3.1 g, Sodium 9 mg

12. Energy Boosting Oatmeal

Preparation Time: 15 Minutes
Cooking Time: 45 Minutes
Servings: 6
INGREDIENTS:
- Oatmeal
- 1½ cups rolled oats
- 1 cup Irish steel-cut oats
- ¼ cup ground flaxseed
- 2 tablespoons chia seeds
- 2 tablespoons pecans, chopped
- 2 large ripe bananas, peeled and mashed
- 2 tablespoons dates, pitted and chopped
- 2 tablespoons peanut butter
- 1 tablespoon coconut oil
- ¾ teaspoon vanilla extract
- ¼ teaspoon sea salt
- ¼ cup water
- Topping
- 1/3 cup fresh berries (blueberries, strawberries)

DIRECTIONS:
1. Preheat the oven to 375°F.
2. Line a 9×13-inch baking dish with parchment paper.
3. Place all of the oatmeal ingredients in a mixing bowl and mix well.

4. Place the oat mixture into the prepared baking dish and press with the back of a spoon to smooth the top surface evenly.
5. Bake for approximately 45 minutes.
6. Remove from oven and let cool slightly before serving.
7. Divide the oatmeal into serving bowls and serve topped with the berries.

NUTRITION: Calories 258, Fat 11.2 g, Carbs 34.9 g, Sugar 8.8 g, Protein 7.1 g, Sodium 125 mg

13. Nutritious Overnight Muesli

Preparation Time: 15 Minutes
Cooking Time: 0 Minutes
Servings: 6
INGREDIENTS:

- Muesli
- 1 cup barley flakes
- 1 cup rye flakes
- 1 cup old-fashioned rolled oats
- ½ cup almonds, slivered
- ½ cup pecans, chopped
- ½ cup raisins, chopped
- ¼ cup raw sunflower seeds
- ¼ cup flaxseed meal
- 2 teaspoons ground cinnamon
- For serving
- 4½ cups unsweetened almond milk (divided)
- 2 kiwifruits, peeled and sliced
- 2 bananas, peeled and sliced

DIRECTIONS:

1. To make the muesli, place all of the ingredients in an airtight container and mix well.
2. Divide the muesli into bowls, add ½ cup of the almond milk to each, and stir to combine.
3. Cover each bowl with plastic wrap and refrigerate for at least 2 hours or overnight.
4. Just before serving, drizzle each bowl with ¼ cup of the remaining almond milk.
5. Top with fruit slices and serve.

NUTRITION: Calories 402, Fat 18.4 g, Carbs 55 g, Sugar 16.1g, Protein 10 g, Sodium 221 mg

14. Egg-Free Tofu Scramble

Preparation Time: 15 Minutes
Cooking Time: 5 Minutes
Servings: 2
INGREDIENTS:

- 1 tablespoon olive oil
- 7 ounces firm tofu, pressed, drained, and crumbled

- ½ small red onion, chopped
- 1 tablespoon almond butter
- 1 teaspoon low-sodium soy sauce
- 1 teaspoon ground turmeric
- Pepper to taste
- ¼ cup water
- 1 large tomato, cut into small chunks
- ¼ cup fresh chives, minced

DIRECTIONS:
1. Heat the olive oil in a medium pan over medium heat and cook the tofu for about 1 minute, stirring frequently.
2. Stir in the onion and cook for about 2 minutes, stirring frequently.
3. Stir in the almond butter, soy sauce, turmeric, and pepper, and cook for about 1 minute, stirring frequently.
4. Stir in the tomato and chives. Remove from heat.
5. Serve hot.

NUTRITION: Calories 208, Fat 16 g, Carbs 9.5 g, Sugar 4.4 g, Protein 11.3 g, Sodium 166 mg

15. Fluffy Tomato Vegan Omelet

Preparation Time: 15 Minutes
Cooking Time: 12 Minutes
Servings: 4
INGREDIENTS:
- 1 cup chickpea flour
- ¼ teaspoon ground turmeric
- ¼ teaspoon red chili powder
- Pinch of ground cumin
- Pinch of sea salt
- 1½–2 cups water
- 1 medium onion, finely chopped
- 2 medium tomatoes, finely chopped
- 1 jalapeno pepper, finely chopped
- 2 tablespoons fresh cilantro, chopped
- 2 tablespoons olive oil (divided)

DIRECTIONS:
1. Add the flour, spices, and sea salt to a large bowl and mix well.
2. Slowly mix in the water.
3. Fold in the onion, tomatoes, jalapeno, and cilantro.
4. Heat ½ tablespoon of the olive oil in a large nonstick frying pan over medium heat.
5. Add half of the tomato mixture and tilt the pan to spread it.
6. Cook for 5–7 minutes.

7. Place the remaining oil over the omelet and carefully flip it over.
8. Cook for about 4–5 minutes or until golden brown.
9. Repeat with the remaining mixture.

NUTRITION: Calories 267, Fat 10.3 g, Carbs 35.7 g, Sugar 21 g, Protein 10.6 g, Sodium 86 mg

16. Best-Ever Oatmeal Muffins

Preparation Time: 10 Minutes
Cooking Time: 20 Minutes
Servings: 4
INGREDIENTS:
- Olive oil cooking spray
- 1 cup oat flour
- 1 cup old-fashioned rolled oats
- ¼ cup flaxseed meal
- ½ teaspoon ground ginger
- 1 ¼ cups unsweetened applesauce
- ½ cup pineapples, chopped
- ¼ cup walnuts, chopped
- 2 teaspoons unsweetened coconut flakes
- 2 teaspoons orange zest, grated

DIRECTIONS:
1. Preheat the oven to 350°F.
2. Lightly grease 8 cups of a muffin tin with the cooking spray.
3. Add the oat flour, oats, flaxseed meal, and ginger to a large mixing bowl and mix well.
4. Add the applesauce and mix well.
5. Add the remaining ingredients and stir gently to combine.
6. Transfer the mixture into the prepared muffin cups.
7. Bake for approximately 20 minutes or until a toothpick inserted in the center comes out clean.
8. Place the muffin tin on a wire rack to cool for about 10 minutes.
9. Carefully invert the muffins onto the wire rack and let cool completely before serving.

NUTRITION: Calories 361, Fat 10.4 g, Carbs 59.7 g, Sugar 26.1 g, Protein 9.2 g, Sodium 6 mg

17. Crust-Less Mushroom Quiches

Preparation Time: 15 Minutes
Cooking Time: 30 Minutes
Servings: 6
INGREDIENTS:
- Olive oil cooking spray
- 1 teaspoon olive oil
- 1½ cups fresh mushrooms, chopped
- 1 scallion, chopped

- 1 teaspoon garlic, minced
- 1 teaspoon fresh rosemary, minced
- Pepper to taste
- 1 (12-ounce) package light firm silken tofu, pressed and drained
- ¼ cup unsweetened soy milk
- 2 tablespoons nutritional yeast
- 1 tablespoon arrowroot starch
- 1 teaspoon coconut oil
- ¼ teaspoon ground turmeric

DIRECTIONS:

1. Preheat the oven to 375°F.
2. Grease a 12-cup muffin tin with cooking spray.
3. Heat the olive oil in a nonstick skillet over medium heat and sauté the scallions and garlic for about 1 minute.
4. Add the mushrooms and sauté for about 5–7 minutes.
5. Stir in the rosemary and pepper. Remove from heat.
6. Set aside to cool slightly.
7. Add the tofu and remaining ingredients to a food processor and pulse until smooth.
8. Transfer the tofu mixture into a large bowl.
9. Fold in the mushroom mixture.
10. Transfer the mixture into the prepared muffin cups.
11. Bake for approximately 20–22 minutes or until the tops become golden brown.
12. Remove the muffin pan from the oven and place it onto a wire rack to cool for about 10 minutes.
13. Carefully invert the muffins onto a platter and serve warm.

NUTRITION: Calories 87, Fat 3.7 g, Carbs 7.4 g, Sugar 21 g, Protein 8 g, Sodium 32 mg

18. Earthy Beans Salad

Preparation Time: 20 Minutes
Cooking Time: 0 Minutes
Servings: 2 to 4
INGREDIENTS:

- Dressing
- 3 tablespoons olive oil
- 2½ tablespoons fresh lime juice
- 1 teaspoon date honey
- 1 clove garlic, minced
- ¼ teaspoon ground cumin
- ¼ teaspoon red chili powder
- Salt and pepper as required
- Salad

- 1 (14½-ounce) can black beans, rinsed and drained
- 1 cup frozen corn, thawed
- 2 cups chopped tomato
- 1 cup seeded and chopped red bell pepper
- ½ red onion, sliced
- 1 English cucumber, chopped
- 1 small jalapeño pepper, seeded and minced
- ½ cup fresh parsley, chopped

DIRECTIONS:
1. To make the dressing, add all of the ingredients to a small jar.
2. Seal the jar and shake to mix well.
3. Place all the salad ingredients in a bowl.
4. Pour the dressing over the salad and toss to coat well.
5. Serve immediately.

Nutrition: Calories 202, Fat 7.9 g, Carbs 27.9 g, Sugar 4.8g, Protein 8 g, Sodium 12 mg

19. Wholesome White and Red Bean and Apple Salad

Preparation Time: 15 Minutes
Cooking Time: 10 Minutes
Servings: 4
INGREDIENTS:
- Dressing
- 3 tablespoons olive oil
- 2 tablespoons balsamic vinegar
- 1 tablespoon date honey
- 2 teaspoons Dijon mustard
- Pepper as required
- Salad
- 2 medium red apples, cored and cubed
- 1 large avocado, peeled, pitted, and cubed
- ¼ cup chopped red onion
- 8 ounces canned red kidney beans, rinsed and drained
- 8 ounces canned white beans, rinsed and drained

DIRECTIONS:
1. To make the dressing, add all of the ingredients to a small jar.
2. Seal the jar and shake to mix well.
3. Place the apples, avocado, onion, and beans in a large salad bowl.
4. Pour the dressing over the salad and toss to coat well.
5. Serve immediately.

NUTRITION: Calories 400, Fat 21.2 g, Carbs 48.5 g, Sugar 17.8 g, Protein 9.1 g, Sodium 314 mg

20. Mediterranean Quinoa Salad

Preparation Time: 15 Minutes
Cooking Time: 20 Minutes
Servings: 2
INGREDIENTS:

- Salad
- 2 cups water
- 1 cup quinoa, rinsed
- ½ cup oil-packed sun-dried tomatoes, drained and chopped
- 2 cups fresh baby arugula
- Dressing
- 2 tablespoons olive oil
- 2 tablespoons fresh lemon juice
- 2 cloves garlic, minced
- 1 teaspoon Dijon mustard
- Pinch of red pepper flakes, crushed
- Salt and pepper as required

DIRECTIONS:

1. To make the quinoa, place the water and quinoa in a medium saucepan over medium-high heat and bring to a boil.
2. Reduce the heat to low and simmer for about 15 minutes or until all the liquid is absorbed.
3. Remove from heat and set aside, covered, for about 5 minutes.
4. Fluff the quinoa with a fork.
5. Add the quinoa, sun-dried tomatoes, and arugula to a salad bowl and mix.
6. To make the dressing, add all of the ingredients to a small jar. Seal the jar and shake to mix well.
7. Pour the dressing over the salad and toss to coat well.
8. Serve immediately.

NUTRITION: Calories 507, Fat 25.4 g, Carbs 68.2 g, Sugar 0.8 g, Protein 14.3 g, Sodium 193 mg

21. Strawberry Mango Shave Ice

Preparation Time: 5 Hours and 30 Minutes
Cooking Time: 0 Minutes
Servings: 3
INGREDIENTS:

- ½ cup superfine sugar, divided
- 1½ cups mango juice
- One diced mango
- 32 oz diced strawberries
- ½ cup coconut, toasted

DIRECTIONS:

1. Combine one cup of water and sugar to a pot over high heat and boil.
2. Remove from heat and add two more cups of water.
3. Freeze this mixture stirring once in 40 minutes.
4. Take a blender and add all remaining ingredients and blend until smooth.
5. Strain into a container with a pouring spout.
6. For serving, add ice into glasses and pour juice and mixture over them.
7. Serve and enjoy.

NUTRITION: Calories 366 Fat 5.5 g Carbohydrates 82.4 g Protein 2.7 g

22. Cinnamon Apples

Preparation Time: 20 Minutes
Cooking Time: 1 Hour
Servings: 4
INGREDIENTS:
- Two apples
- 1 tsp cinnamon

DIRECTIONS:
1. Pre-heat stove to 220°F.
2. Core the apples or cut them into rounds with a sharp blade or mandolin slicer. Place the ingredients in a bowl and drizzle them with cinnamon. Use your hands to make sure the apples are coated completely.
3. Arrange the apple cuts in a single layer on a silicone tray or a baking sheet lined with parchment paper.
4. Bake for 1 hour then turn over the apples.
5. Bake for one more hour. Then, turn the oven off and leave the sheet in the stove until it cooled down.
6. Serve when needed or store in a sealed container for up to a week.

NUTRITION: Calories 33 Fat 0.1 g Carbohydrates 9.1 g Protein 0.2 g

23. Roasted Chickpeas

Preparation Time: 10 Minutes
Cooking Time: 25 Minutes
Servings: 4
INGREDIENTS:
- One can make chickpea, rinsed, drained
- 2 tsp freshly squeezed lemon juice
- 2 tsp tamari
- ½ tsp fresh rosemary, chopped
- 1/8 tsp sea salt
- 1/8 tsp pure maple syrup or agave nectar

DIRECTIONS:
1. Preheat stove to 400°F. Line a baking sheet with parchment paper.
2. Toss all ingredients together and spread the chickpeas out on the baking sheet.
3. Roast for around 25 minutes, stirring the chickpeas every 5 minutes or so. Note, until the tamari and lemon juice dry up, the chickpeas will seem delicate, not crunchy.
4. Serve hot or at room warmth for a snack.

NUTRITION: Calories 290 Fat 10.2 g Carbohydrates 40.3 g Protein 10.9 g

24. Baked Sesame Fries

Preparation Time: 10 Minutes

Cooking Time: 20 Minutes

Servings: 4

INGREDIENTS:

- 1 lb. Yukon potatoes, gold, cut into wedges, unpeeled
- 1 tbsp avocado, grapeseed
- 2 tbsp, seeds, sesame
- 1 tbsp potato starch
- 1 tbsp, yeast nutritional
- Generous pinch salt
- Black pepper

DIRECTIONS:

1. Preheat stove to 425°F.
2. Delicately oil a baking sheet of metal or line it with parchment paper.
3. Toss potatoes with all the ingredients until covered; if seeds do not stick, drizzle a little more oil.
4. Scattered potatoes in an even layer onto the prepared sheet and bake for 20 to 25 minutes, tossing once halfway through, until the potatoes become crispy.
5. Serve with desired toppings.

NUTRITION: Calories 192 Fat 5.9 g Carbohydrates 32.6 g Protein 2.8 g

25. No-Bake Coconut Chia Macaroons

Preparation Time: 2 Hours

Cooking Time: 0 Minutes

Servings: 6

INGREDIENTS:

- 1 cup Shredded Coconut
- 2 tbsp Chia Seeds
- ½ cup Coconut Cream
- ½ cup Erythritol

DIRECTIONS:

1. Combine all ingredients in a bowl. Mix until well combined.
2. Chill the mixture for about half or a quarter of an hour.
3. Once set, scoop the mixture into serving portions and roll into balls.
4. Return to the chiller for another hour.

NUTRITION: Calories 129 Carbohydrates 5 g Fats 12 g Protein 2 g

26. Vegan Fudge Revel Bars

Preparation Time: 1 Hour

Cooking Time: Minutes

Servings: 12

INGREDIENTS:

- 1 cup Almond Flour
- ¾ cup Erythritol
- ¾ cup Peanut Butter
- 1 tbsp Vanilla extract
- ½ cup Sugar-Free Chocolate Chips
- 2 tbsp Margarine

DIRECTIONS:
1. Mix almond butter, coconut flour, erythritol, and vanilla extract in a bowl until well combined.
2. Press the mixture into a rectangular silicone mold and freeze for an hour to set.
3. Melt the chocolate chips with the margarine for 1-2 minutes in the microwave.
4. Pour melt down chocolate on top of the mold and chill for another hour to set.
5. Slice for serving.

NUTRITION: Calories 160 Carbohydrates 5 g Fats 14 g Protein 5 g

27. Risotto Bites

Preparation Time: 15 Minutes
Cooking Time: 20 Minutes
Servings: 12
INGREDIENTS:

- ½ cup panko breadcrumbs
- One teaspoon paprika
- One teaspoon chipotle powder or ground cayenne pepper
- 1½ cups cold Green Pea Risotto
- Nonstick cooking spray

DIRECTIONS:
1. Preheat the oven to 425°F. Line a baking sheet with parchment paper.
2. On a large plate, combine the panko, paprika, and chipotle powder. Set aside.
3. Roll two tablespoons of the risotto into a ball. Gently roll in the breadcrumbs, and place on the prepared baking sheet. Repeat to make a total of 12 balls.
4. Spritz the tops of the risotto bites with nonstick cooking spray and bake for 15 to 20 minutes, until they begin to brown.
5. Cool totally before storing it in a large airtight container in a single layer (add a piece of parchment paper for a second layer) or a plastic freezer bag.

NUTRITION: Calories: 100 Fat: 2g Protein: 6g Carbohydrates: 17g Fiber: 5g Sugar: 2g Sodium: 165mg

28. Taco Pita Pizzas

Preparation Time: 5 Minutes
Cooking Time: 7 Minutes
Servings: 4
INGREDIENTS:

- Four sandwich-size pita bread pieces or Sandwich Thins
- 1 cup vegetarian refried beans
- 1 cup pizza sauce
- 1 cup chopped mushrooms
- One teaspoon minced jalapeño (optional)

DIRECTIONS:

1. Preheat the oven to 400°F.
2. Assemble four pizzas: On each pita, spread about ¼ cup of refried beans. Pour ¼ cup of pizza sauce over the beans and spread evenly. Add ¼ cup of mushrooms. Sprinkle ¼ teaspoon of minced jalapeño (if using) over the mushrooms.
3. Place the pizzas on the ready baking sheet and bake for 7 minutes.
4. Cool completely before placing each pizza in a freezer-safe plastic bag or store together in one large airtight, freezer-safe container with parchment paper between the pizzas.

NUTRITION: Calories: 148 Fat: 2g Protein: 6g Carbohydrates: 29g Fiber: 5g Sugar: 3g Sodium: 492mg

29. Savory Seed Crackers

Preparation Time: 5 Minutes
Cooking Time: 50 Minutes
Servings: 20
INGREDIENTS:

- ¾ cup pumpkin seeds (pepitas)
- ½ cup sunflower seeds
- ½ cup sesame seeds
- ¼ cup chia seeds
- One teaspoon minced garlic (about one clove)
- One teaspoon tamari or soy sauce
- One teaspoon vegan Worcestershire sauce
- ½ teaspoon ground cayenne pepper
- ½ teaspoon dried oregano
- ½ cup of water

DIRECTIONS:

1. Preheat the oven to 325°F. Line Up a rimmed baking sheet with parchment paper.
2. In a large bowl, combine the pumpkin seeds, sunflower seeds, sesame seeds, chia seeds, garlic, tamari, Worcestershire sauce, cayenne, oregano, and water. Move to the prepared baking sheet, spreading out to all sides.
3. Bake for 25 minutes. Remove the pan from the oven and flip the seed "dough" over so the wet side is up. Bake for an extra 20 to 25 minutes, until the sides are browned.
4. Cool completely before breaking up into 20 pieces. Divide evenly among four glass jars and close tightly with lids.

NUTRITION: Calories: 339 Fat: 29g Protein: 14g Carbohydrates: 17g Fiber: 8g Sugar: 1g Sodium: 96mg

30. Tamari Almonds

Preparation Time: 5 Minutes
Cooking Time: 25 Minutes
Servings: 8
INGREDIENTS:

- 1-pound raw almonds
- Three tablespoons tamari or soy sauce
- Two tablespoons extra-virgin olive oil
- One tablespoon nutritional yeast
- 1 to 2 teaspoons chili residue, to taste

DIRECTIONS:

1. Preheat the oven to 400°F. Line a baking sheet with parchment paper.
2. In a medium bowl, combine the almonds, tamari, and olive oil until well coated. Spread the almonds on the prepared baking sheet and roast for 10 to 15 minutes, until browned.
3. Cool for 10 minutes, then season with the nutritional yeast and chili powder.
4. Transfer to a glass jar and close tightly with a lid.

NUTRITION: Calories: 364 Fat: 32g Protein: 13g Carbohydrates: 13g Fiber: 7g Sugar: 3g Sodium: 381mg

31. Potato Carrot Salad

Preparation Time: 15 Minutes
Cooking Time: 10 Minutes
Servings: 6
INGREDIENTS:

- Water
- Six potatoes, sliced into cubes
- Three carrots, sliced into cubes
- One tablespoon milk
- One tablespoon Dijon mustard
- ¼ cup mayonnaise
- Pepper to taste
- Two teaspoons fresh thyme, chopped
- One stalk celery, chopped
- Two scallions, chopped
- One slice turkey bacon, cooked crispy and crumbled

DIRECTIONS:

1. Fill your pot with water.
2. Place it over medium-high heat.
3. Boil the potatoes and carrots for 10 to 15 minutes or until tender.
4. Drain and let cool.
5. In a bowl, mix the milk mustard, mayo, pepper, and thyme.

6. Stir in the potatoes, carrots, and celery.
7. Coat evenly with the sauce.
8. Cover and refrigerate for 4 hours.
9. Top with the scallions and turkey bacon bits before serving.

NUTRITION: Calories 106 Fat 5.3 g Saturated fat 1 g Carbohydrates 12.6 g Fiber 1.8g Protein 2 g

32. Mediterranean Salad

Preparation Time: 20 Minutes
Cooking Time: 5 Minutes
Servings: 2
INGREDIENTS:

- Two teaspoons balsamic vinegar
- One tablespoon basil pesto
- 1 cup lettuce
- ¼ cup broccoli florets, chopped
- ½ cup zucchini, chopped
- ¼ cup tomato, chopped
- ¼ cup yellow bell pepper, chopped
- Two tablespoons feta cheese, crumbled

DIRECTIONS:
1. Arrange the lettuce on a serving platter.
2. Top with the broccoli, zucchini, tomato, and bell pepper.
3. In a bowl, mix the vinegar and pesto.
4. Drizzle the dressing on top.
5. Sprinkle the feta cheese and serve.

NUTRITION: Calories 100 Fat 6 g Saturated fat 1 g Carbohydrates 7 g Protein 4 g

33. High Protein Salad

Preparation Time: 5 Minutes
Cooking Time: 5 Minutes
Servings: 4
INGREDIENTS:

- Salad:
- One 15-oz can green kidney beans
- 2 4 tbsp capers
- 3 4 handfuls arugula
- 4 15-oz can lentils
- Dressing:
- 1 tbsp caper brine
- 1 tbsp tamari
- 1 tbsp balsamic vinegar

- 2 tbsp peanut butter
- 2 tbsp hot sauce
- 1 tbsp tahini

DIRECTIONS:
1. For the dressing:
2. In a bowl, stir together all the materials until they come together to form a smooth dressing.
3. For the salad:
4. Mix the beans, arugula, capers, and lentils. Top with the dressing and serve.

NUTRITION: Calories: 205 Fat: 2 g Protein: 13 g Carbs: 31 g Fiber: 17g

34. Avocado Fries

Preparation Time: 10 Minutes
Cooking Time: 7 Minutes
Servings: 6
INGREDIENTS:
- One avocado
- ½ tsp. salt
- ½ C. panko breadcrumbs
- Bean liquid (aquafaba) from a 15-ounce can of white or garbanzo beans

DIRECTIONS:
1. Preparing the Ingredients. Peel, pit, and slice up avocado.
2. Toss salt and breadcrumbs together in a bowl. Place aquafaba into another bowl.
3. Dredge slices of avocado first in aquafaba and then in panko, making sure you can even coating.
4. Air Frying. Place coated avocado slices into a single layer in the Instant Crisp Air Fryer. Set temperature to 390°F and set time to 5 minutes.
5. Serve with your favorite keto dipping sauce!

NUTRITION: Calories: 102 Fat: 22g Protein: 9g Sugar: 1g

35. Crispy Jalapeno Coins

Preparation Time: 10 Minutes
Cooking Time: 5 Minutes
Servings: 2
INGREDIENTS:
- One egg
- 2-3 tbsp. coconut flour
- One sliced and seeded jalapeno
- Pinch of garlic powder
- Pinch of onion powder
- Pinch of Cajun seasoning (optional)
- Pinch of pepper and salt

DIRECTIONS:

1. Preparing the Ingredients. Ensure your Instant Crisp Air Fryer is preheated to 400 degrees.
2. Mix all dry ingredients.
3. Pat jalapeno slices dry. Dip coins into the egg wash and then into the dry mixture. Toss to coat thoroughly.
4. Add coated jalapeno slices to Instant Crisp Air Fryer in a singular layer. Spray with olive oil.
5. Air Frying. Lock the air fryer lid. Set temperature to 350°F and set time to 5 minutes. Cook just till crispy.

NUTRITION: Calories: 128 Fat: 8g Protein: 7g Sugar: 0g

36. Zucchini Parmesan Chips

Preparation Time: 10 Minutes
Cooking Time: 8 Minutes
Servings: 10
INGREDIENTS:

- ½ tsp. paprika
- ½ C. grated parmesan cheese
- ½ C. Italian breadcrumbs
- One lightly beaten egg
- Two thinly sliced zucchinis

DIRECTIONS:

1. Preparing the Ingredients. Use a very sharp knife or mandolin slicer to slice zucchini as thinly as you can. Pat off extra moisture.
2. Beat egg with a pinch of pepper and salt and a bit of water.
3. Combine paprika, cheese, and breadcrumbs in a bowl.
4. Dip slices of zucchini into the egg mixture and then into breadcrumb mixture. Press gently to coat.
5. Air Frying. With olive oil cooking spray, mist coated zucchini slices. Place into your Instant Crisp Air Fryer in a single layer. Lock the air fryer lid. Set temperature to 350°F and set time to 8 minutes.
6. Sprinkle with salt and serve with salsa.

NUTRITION: Calories: 211 Fat: 16g Protein: 8g Sugar: 0g

37. Jalapeno Cheese Balls

Preparation Time: 10 Minutes
Cooking Time: 8 Minutes
Servings: 12
INGREDIENTS:

- 4 ounces cream cheese
- 1/3 cup shredded mozzarella cheese
- 1/3 cup shredded Cheddar cheese
- Two jalapeños, finely chopped

- ½ cup breadcrumbs
- Two eggs
- ½ cup all-purpose flour
- Salt
- Pepper
- Cooking oil

DIRECTIONS:

1. Preparing the Ingredients. Combine the cream cheese, mozzarella, Cheddar, and jalapeños in a medium bowl. Mix well.
2. Form the cheese mixture into balls about an inch thick. You may also use a small ice cream scoop. It works well.
3. Arrange the cheese balls on a sheet pan and place in the freezer for 15 minutes. It will help the cheese balls maintain their shape while frying.
4. Spray the Instant Crisp Air Fryer basket with cooking oil. Place the breadcrumbs in a small bowl. In another small bowl, beat the eggs. In the third small bowl, combine the flour with salt and pepper to taste, and mix well. Remove the cheese balls from the freezer. Plunge the cheese balls in the flour, then the eggs, and then the breadcrumbs.
5. Air Frying. Place the cheese balls in the Instant Crisp Air Fryer. Spray with cooking oil. Lock the air fryer lid—Cook for 8 minutes.
6. Open the Instant Crisp Air Fryer and flip the cheese balls. I recommend flipping them instead of shaking, so the balls maintain their form. Cook an additional 4 minutes. Cool before serving.

NUTRITION: Calories: 96 Fat: 6g Protein: 4g Sugar: 0g

38. Air Fryer Asparagus

Preparation Time: 5 Minutes
Cooking Time: 8 Minutes
Servings: 2
INGREDIENTS:

- Nutritional yeast
- Olive oil non-stick spray
- One bunch of asparagus

DIRECTIONS:

1. Preparing the Ingredients. Wash asparagus. Do not forget to trim off thick, woody ends.
2. Spray asparagus with olive oil spray and sprinkle with yeast.
3. Air Frying. In your Instant Crisp Air Fryer, lay asparagus in a singular layer. Set the temperature to 360°F. While the time limit to 8 minutes.

NUTRITION: Calories: 17 Fat: 4g Protein: 9g

39. Cheesy Cauliflower Fritters

Preparation Time: 10 Minutes
Cooking Time: 7 Minutes

Servings: 8

INGREDIENTS:

- ½ C. chopped parsley
- 1 C. Italian breadcrumbs
- 1/3 C. shredded mozzarella cheese
- 1/3 C. shredded sharp cheddar cheese
- One egg
- Two minced garlic cloves
- Three chopped scallions
- One head of cauliflower

DIRECTIONS:

1. Preparing the Ingredients. Cut the cauliflower up into florets. Wash well and pat dry. Place into a food processor and pulse 20-30 seconds till it looks like rice.
2. Place the cauliflower rice in a bowl and mix with pepper, salt, egg, cheeses, breadcrumbs, garlic, and scallions.
3. With hands, form 15 patties of the mixture then add more breadcrumbs if needed.
4. Air Frying. With olive oil, spritz patties, and place into your Instant Crisp Air Fryer in a single layer. Lock the air fryer lid. Set temperature to 390°F, and set time to 7 minutes, flipping after 7 minutes.

NUTRITION: Calories: 209 Fat: 17g Protein: 6g Sugar: 0.5

40. Arugula Salad

Preparation Time: 15 Minutes
Cooking Time: 0 Minutes
Servings: 4

INGREDIENTS:

- 6 cups fresh arugula leaves
- 2 cups radicchio, chopped
- ¼ cup low-fat balsamic vinaigrette
- ¼ cup pine nuts, toasted and chopped

DIRECTIONS:

1. Arrange the arugula leaves in a serving bowl.
2. Sprinkle the radicchio on top.
3. Drizzle with the vinaigrette.
4. Sprinkle the pine nuts on top.

NUTRITION: Calories 85 Fat 6.6 g Saturated fat 0.5 g Carbohydrates 5.1 g Fiber 1 g Protein 2.2 g

41. Grilled Veggie Kabobs

Preparation Time: 15 Minutes
Cooking Time: 12 to 15 Minutes
Servings: 6
INGREDIENTS:

- Marinade:
- ½ cup balsamic vinegar
- 1½ tablespoons minced thyme
- 1½ tablespoons minced rosemary
- Three cloves garlic, peeled and minced
- Sea salt, to taste (optional)
- Freshly ground black pepper, to taste
- Veggies:
- 2 cups cherry tomatoes
- One red bell pepper, it should be seeded and cut into 1-inch pieces
- One green bell pepper, without seeds and cut into 1-inch pieces
- One medium yellow squash, cut into 1-inch rounds
- One medium zucchini, cut into 1-inch rounds
- One medium red onion skinned and cut into large chunks

- Special Equipment:
- 12 bamboo skewers, make sure to soak it in water for 30 minutes

DIRECTIONS:
1. Preheat the grill to medium heat.
2. In making the marinade: In a small bowl, stir together the balsamic vinegar, thyme, rosemary, garlic, salt (if desired), and pepper.
3. Thread veggies onto skewers, alternating between different-colored veggies.
4. Grill the veggies for 12 to 15 minutes until softened and lightly charred, brushing the veggies with the marinade and flipping the skewers every 4 to 5 minutes.
5. Remove from the grill and serve hot.

NUTRITION: Calories: 98 Fat: 0.7g Carbs: 19.2g Protein: 3.8g Fiber: 3.4g

42. Grilled Cauliflower Steaks

Preparation Time: 10 Minutes
Cooking Time: 57 Minutes
Servings: 4
INGREDIENTS:
- Two medium heads cauliflower
- Two medium shallots, peeled and minced
- Water, as needed
- One clove garlic, peeled and minced
- ½ teaspoon ground fennel
- ½ teaspoon minced sage
- ½ teaspoon crushed red pepper flakes
- ½ cup green lentils, rinsed
- 2 cups low-sodium vegetable broth
- Salt, to taste (optional)
- Freshly ground black pepper, to taste
- Chopped parsley, for garnish

DIRECTIONS:
1. On a flat work surface, cut each of the cauliflower heads in half through the stem, then trim each half, so you get a 1-inch-thick steak.
2. Arrange each piece on a baking sheet and set aside. You can reserve the extra cauliflower florets for other uses.
3. Sauté the shallots in a medium saucepan over medium heat for 10 minutes, stirring occasionally. Add water, 1 to 3 tablespoons at a time, to keep the shallots from sticking.
4. Stir in the garlic, fennel, sage, red pepper flakes, and lentils and cook for 3 minutes.
5. Pour into the vegetable broth and bring to a boil over high heat.
6. Reduce the heat to medium, cover, and cook for 45 to 50 minutes, or until the lentils are very soft, adding more water as needed.
7. Using an immersion blender, purée the mixture until smooth. Sprinkle with salt (if desired) and pepper. Keep warm and set aside.

8. Preheat the grill to medium heat.
9. Grill the cauliflower steaks for about 7 minutes per side until evenly browned.
10. Transfer the cauliflower steaks to a plate and spoon the purée over them. Serve garnished with the parsley.

NUTRITION: Calories: 105 Fat: 1.1g Carbs: 18.3g Protein: 5.4g Fiber: 4.9g

43. Vegetable Hash with White Beans

Preparation Time: 15 Minutes
Cooking Time: 23 Minutes
Servings: 4
INGREDIENTS:
- One leek (white part only), finely chopped
- One red bell pepper, deseeded and diced
- Water, as needed
- Two teaspoons minced rosemary
- Three cloves garlic, peeled and minced
- One medium sweet potato, peeled and diced
- One large turnip, peeled and diced
- 2 cups cooked white beans, or 1 (15-ounce / 425-g) can drain and rinse
- Zest and juice of 1 orange
- 1 cup chopped kale
- Salt, to taste (optional)
- Freshly ground black pepper, to taste

DIRECTIONS:
1. Put the leek and red pepper in a large saucepan over medium heat and sauté for 8 minutes, stirring occasionally. Add water, 1 to 3 tablespoons at a time, to keep them from sticking to the bottom of the pan.
2. Stir in the rosemary and garlic and sauté for 1 minute more.
3. Add the sweet potato, turnip, beans, and orange juice and zest, and stir well—heat until the vegetables are softened.
4. Add the kale and sprinkle with salt (if desired) and pepper. Cook for about 5 minutes or more until the kale is wilted.
5. Serve on a plate.

NUTRITION: Calories: 245 Fat: 0.6g Carbs: 48.0g Protein: 11.9g Fiber: 9.3g

44. Ratatouille

Preparation Time: 20 Minutes
Cooking Time: 25 Minutes
Servings: 4
INGREDIENTS:
- One medium red onion, peeled and diced

- Water, as needed
- Four cloves garlic, peeled and minced
- One medium red bell pepper, without seeds and diced
- One small zucchini, diced
- One medium eggplant stemmed and diced
- One large tomato, diced
- ½ cup chopped basil
- Salt, to taste (optional)
- Freshly ground black pepper, to taste

DIRECTIONS:

1. Put the onion in a medium saucepan over medium heat and sauté for 10 minutes, stirring occasionally, or until the onion is tender. Add water 1 to 3 tablespoons at a time to keep it from sticking.
2. Add the garlic, red pepper, zucchini, and eggplant and stir well. Lid the saucepan and cook for 12 to 15 minutes, stirring occasionally.
3. Mix in the tomatoes and basil, then sprinkle with salt (if desired) and pepper. Serve immediately.

NUTRITION: Calories: 76 Fat: 0.5g Carbs: 15.3g Protein: 2.7g Fiber: 5.9g

45. Baingan Bharta (Indian Spiced Eggplant)

Preparation Time: 15 Minutes
Cooking Time: 25 Minutes
Servings: 4
INGREDIENTS:

- Two medium onions, peeled and diced
- One large red bell pepper, deseeded and diced
- Water, as needed
- Two large tomatoes, finely chopped
- Two medium eggplants, stemmed, peeled, and cut into ½-inch dices
- Three tablespoons grated ginger
- One teaspoon coriander seed, toasted and ground
- Two teaspoons cumin seeds, toasted and ground
- ½ teaspoon crushed red pepper flakes
- Pinch cloves
- Salt, to taste (optional)
- ½ bunch cilantro, leaves, and tender stems, finely sliced

DIRECTIONS:

1. Combine the onions and red pepper in a large saucepan and cook over medium heat for about 10 to 12 minutes. Include water 1 to 2 tablespoons at the moment to keep them from sticking to the pan.

2. Stir in the tomatoes, eggplant, ginger, coriander, cumin, crushed red pepper flakes, and cloves and cook for just about 12 to 15 minutes, or until the vegetables are tender.
3. Sprinkle with the salt, if desired. Garnish with the cilantro and serve warm.

NUTRITION: Calories: 140 Fat: 1.1g Carbs: 27.9g Protein: 4.7g Fiber: 10.9g

46. Cauliflower and Potato Curry

Preparation Time: 10 Minutes
Cooking Time: 27 Minutes
Servings: 4
INGREDIENTS:

- One medium yellow onion, peeled and diced
- Water, as needed
- Two cloves garlic, peeled and minced
- One tablespoon grated ginger
- ½ jalapeño pepper, deseeded and minced
- One medium head cauliflower, cut into florets
- Two medium tomatoes, diced
- 1-pound (454 g) Yukon Gold potatoes, cut into ½-inch dices
- One teaspoon ground coriander
- One teaspoon ground cumin
- One teaspoon crushed red pepper flakes
- ½ teaspoon turmeric
- ¼ teaspoon ground cloves
- Two bay leaves
- 1 cup green peas
- ¼ cup chopped cilantro or mint, for garnish

DIRECTIONS:
1. Sauté the onion in a large pot over low to medium heat for 7 to 8 minutes, stirring occasionally. Add water, 1 to 3 tablespoons at a time, to keep it from sticking to the pan.
2. Stir in the garlic, ginger, and jalapeño pepper and sauté for 3 minutes.
3. Add the cauliflower, tomatoes, potatoes, coriander, cumin, crushed red pepper flakes, turmeric, cloves, and bay leaves and stir to combine—cover and cook for 12 to 15 minutes, or until the vegetables are soft.
4. Mix in the peas and cook for an additional 5 minutes.
5. Remove the bay leaves and sprinkle the chopped cilantro on top for garnish. Serve immediately.

NUTRITION: Calories: 175 Fat: 0.9g Carbs: 34.9g Protein: 6.7g Fiber: 7.5g

47. Kale and Pinto Bean Enchilada Casserole

Preparation Time: 10 Minutes
Cooking Time: 30 Minutes

Servings: 8

INGREDIENTS:

- One teaspoon olive oil (optional)
- One yellow onion, diced
- One bunch kale stemmed and chopped
- Two teaspoons Taco Seasoning
- 2 to 3 cups cooked pinto beans, or 2 (15-ounce / 425-g) cans pinto beans, drained and rinsed
- Sea salt, to taste (optional)
- Black pepper, to taste
- 1 (16-ounce / 454-g) jar salsa (any variety), divided
- 12 corn tortillas
- ½ cup cashew queso, or more to taste

DIRECTIONS:

1. Preheat the oven to 350°F (205°C). Grease a baking dish with the olive oil, if desired.
2. Place the onion, kale, taco seasoning, and beans in the dish. Sprinkle with salt (if desired) and pepper. Drizzle half the salsa over the beans. Place the tortillas on top. Scatter with the remaining salsa and cashew queso.
3. Cover the dish with aluminum foil and bake in the preheated oven for about 30 minutes, or until the vegetables are warm and the salsa bubbles.
4. Let it cool for 10 minutes before slicing and serving.

NUTRITION: Calories: 194 Fat: 3.8g Carbs: 29.0g Protein: 10.9g Fiber: 9.4g

48. Potato and Zucchini Casserole

Preparation Time: 10 Minutes
Cooking Time: 1 hour
Servings: 6
INGREDIENTS:

- Three large russet potatoes halved lengthwise and thinly sliced
- Three medium zucchinis halved lengthwise and thinly sliced
- ¾ cup nutritional yeast
- ¾ cup diced green or red bell pepper (about one small bell pepper)
- ¾ cup diced red, white, or yellow onion (about one small onion)
- ½ cup dry breadcrumbs
- ¼ cup olive oil (optional)
- 1½ teaspoons minced garlic (about three small cloves)
- Pepper, to taste
- Sea salt, to taste (optional)

DIRECTIONS:

1. Preheat the oven to 400°F.
2. Mix all the ingredients.
3. Place the mixture in a large cooking pot dish.

4. Bake in the preheated oven for 1 hour until heated through, stirring once halfway through.
5. Take off from the oven and allow to cool for 5 minutes before serving.

NUTRITION: Calories: 352 Fat: 10.0g Carbs: 51.5g Protein: 14.1g Fiber: 5.5g

49. Broccoli Casserole with Beans and Walnuts

Preparation Time: 10 Minutes
Cooking Time: 35-40 Minutes
Servings: 4
INGREDIENTS:

- ¾ cup vegetable broth
- Two broccoli heads, crowns, and stalks finely chopped
- One teaspoon salt (optional)
- 2 cups cooked pinto or navy beans
- 1 to 2 tablespoons brown rice flour or arrowroot flour
- 1 cup chopped walnuts

DIRECTIONS:

1. Preheat the oven to 400°F (205°C).
2. Warm the vegetable broth in a large ovenproof pot over medium heat.
3. Add the broccoli and season with salt, if desired, then cook for 6 to 8 minutes, stirring occasionally, or until the broccoli is light green.
4. Add the pinto beans and brown rice flour to the skillet and stir well. Sauté for another 5 to 7 minutes, or until the liquid thickens slightly. Scatter the top with the walnuts.
5. Transfer the pot to the oven. Bake it until the walnuts are toasted, 20 to 25 minutes.
6. Let the casserole cool for 8 to 10 minutes in the pot before serving.

NUTRITION: Calories: 412 Fat: 20.2g Carbs: 43.3g Protein: 21.6g Fiber: 13.1g

50. Pistachio Crusted Tofu

Preparation Time: 10 Minutes
Cooking Time: 20 Minutes
Servings: 8
INGREDIENTS:

- ½ cup roasted, shelled pistachios
- ¼ cup whole wheat breadcrumbs
- One garlic clove, minced
- One shallot, minced
- ½ teaspoon dried tarragon
- One teaspoon grated lemon zest
- Sea salt, to taste (optional)
- Black pepper, to taste
- 1 (16-ounce / 454-g) package sprouted or extra-firm tofu, drained and sliced lengthwise into eight pieces

- One tablespoon Dijon mustard
- One tablespoon lemon juice

DIRECTIONS:

1. Warm up the oven to 400ºF (205ºC). Line a baking sheet with parchment paper.
2. Then place the pistachios in a food processor until they are about the size of the breadcrumbs. Mix the pistachios, breadcrumbs, garlic, shallot, tarragon, and lemon zest in a shallow dish. Sprinkle with salt (if desired) and pepper. Set aside.
3. Sprinkle the tofu with salt (if desired) and pepper. Mix the mustard and lemon juice in a small bowl and stir well.
4. Brush all over the tofu with the mustard mixture, then coat each slice with the pistachio mixture.
5. Arrange the tofu on the baking sheet. Scatter any remaining pistachio mixture over the slices.
6. Bake in the warmed oven for about 18 to 20 minutes, or until the tofu is browned and crispy.
7. Serve hot.

NUTRITION: Calories: 159 Fat: 9.3g Carbs: 8.3g Protein: 10.4g Fiber: 1.6g

51. Instant Savory Gigante Beans

Preparation Time: 10-30 Minutes
Cooking Time: 55 Minutes
Servings: 6
INGREDIENTS:

- 1 lb. Gigante Beans soaked overnight
- 1/2 cup olive oil
- One onion sliced
- Two cloves garlic crushed or minced
- One red bell pepper (cut into 1/3-inch pieces)
- Two carrots, sliced
- 1/2 tsp salt and ground black pepper
- Two tomatoes peeled, grated
- 1 Tbsp celery (chopped)
- 1 tbsp tomato paste (or ketchup)
- 3/4 tsp sweet paprika
- 1 tsp oregano
- 1 cup vegetable broth

DIRECTIONS:

1. Soak Gigante beans overnight.
2. Press the SAUTÉ button on your Instant Pot and heat the oil.
3. Sauté onion, garlic, sweet pepper, carrots with a pinch of salt for 3 - 4 minutes; stir occasionally.
4. Add rinsed Gigante beans into your Instant Pot along with all remaining ingredients and stir well.
5. Latch lid into place and set on the MANUAL setting for 25 minutes.

6. When the beep sounds, quick release the pressure by pressing Cancel and twisting the steam handle to the Venting position.
7. Taste and adjust seasonings to taste.
8. Serve warm or cold.
9. Keep refrigerated.

NUTRITION: Calories 502.45 Calories From, Fat 173.16 Total Fat 19.63g Saturated Fat 2.86g

52. Instant Turmeric Risotto

Preparation Time: 10-30 Minutes
Cooking Time: 40 Minutes
Servings: 4
INGREDIENTS:
- 4 Tbsp olive oil
- 1 cup onion
- 1 tsp minced garlic
- 2 cups long-grain rice
- 3 cups vegetable broth
- 1/2 tsp paprika (smoked)
- 1/2 tsp turmeric
- 1/2 tsp nutmeg
- 2 Tbsp fresh basil leaves chopped
- Salt and ground black pepper to taste

DIRECTIONS:
1. Press the SAUTÉ button on your Instant Pot and heat oil.
2. Sauté the onion and garlic with a pinch of salt until softened.
3. Add the rice and all leftover ingredients and stir well.
4. Lock the lid into place and set on and select the RICE button for 10 minutes.
5. Press Cancel when the timer beeps and carefully flip the Quick Release valve to let the pressure out.
6. Taste and adjust seasonings to taste.
7. Serve.

NUTRITION: Calories 559.81 Calories from Fat 162.48 Total Fat 18.57g Saturated Fat 2.4g

53. Nettle Soup with Rice

Preparation Time: 10-30 Minutes
Cooking Time: 40 Minutes
Servings: 5
INGREDIENTS:
- 3 Tbsp of olive oil
- Two onions finely chopped
- Two cloves garlic finely chopped

- Salt and freshly ground black pepper
- Four medium potatoes cut into cubes
- 1 cup of rice
- 1 Tbsp arrowroot
- 2 cups vegetable broth
- 2 cups of water
- One bunch of young nettle leaves packed
- 1/2 cup fresh parsley finely chopped
- 1 tsp cumin

DIRECTIONS:
1. Heat olive oil in a large pot.
2. Sauté onion and garlic with a pinch of salt until softened.
3. Add potato, rice, and arrowroot; sauté for 2 to 3 minutes.
4. Pour broth and water, stir well, cover and cook over medium heat for about 20 minutes.
5. Cook for about 30 to 45 minutes.
6. Add young nettle leaves, parsley, and cumin; stir and cook for 5 to 7 minutes.
7. Move the soup in a blender and blend until combined well.
8. Taste and adjust salt and pepper.
9. Serve hot.

NUTRITION: Calories 421.76 Calories from Fat 88.32 Total Fat 9.8g Saturated Fat 1.54g

54. Okra with Grated Tomatoes (Slow Cooker)

Preparation Time: 10-30 Minutes
Cooking Time: 3 Hours and 10 Minutes
Servings: 4
INGREDIENTS:
- 2 lbs. fresh okra cleaned
- Two onions finely chopped
- Two cloves garlic finely sliced
- Two carrots sliced
- Two ripe tomatoes grated
- 1 cup of water
- 4 Tbsp olive oil
- Salt and ground black pepper
- 1 tbsp fresh parsley finely chopped

DIRECTIONS:
1. Add okra in your Crock-Pot: sprinkle with a pinch of salt and pepper.
2. Add in chopped onion, garlic, carrots, and grated tomatoes; stir well.
3. Pour water and oil, season with the salt, pepper, and give a good stir.
4. Covering and cook on LOW for 2-4 hours or until tender.
5. Open the lid and add fresh parsley; stir.

6. Taste and adjust salt and pepper.
7. Serve hot.

NUTRITION: Calories 223.47 Calories from Fat 123.5 Total Fat 14g Saturated Fat 1.96g,

55. Oven-Baked Smoked Lentil Burgers

Preparation Time: 10-30 Minutes
Cooking Time: 1 Hour and 20 Minutes
Servings: 6
INGREDIENTS:

- 1 1/2 cups dried lentils
- 3 cups of water
- Salt and ground black pepper to taste
- 2 Tbsp olive oil
- One onion finely diced
- Two cloves minced garlic
- 1 cup button mushrooms sliced
- 2 Tbsp tomato paste
- 1/2 tsp fresh basil finely chopped
- 1 cup chopped almonds
- 3 tsp balsamic vinegar
- 3 Tbsp coconut amino
- 1 tsp liquid smoke
- 3/4 cup silken tofu soft
- 3/4 cup corn starch

DIRECTIONS:
1. Cook lentils in salted water until tender or for about 30-35 minutes; rinse, drain, and set aside.
2. Heat oil in a frying skillet and sauté onion, garlic, and mushrooms for 4 to 5 minutes; stir occasionally.
3. Stir in the tomato paste, salt, basil, salt, and black pepper; cook for 2 to 3 minutes.
4. Stir in almonds, vinegar, coconut amino, liquid smoke, and lentils.
5. Remove from heat and stir in blended tofu and corn starch.
6. Keep stirring until all ingredients combined well.
7. Form mixture into patties and refrigerate for an hour.
8. Preheat oven to 350 F.
9. Line a baking dish with parchment paper and arrange patties on the pan.
10. Bake for 20 to 25 minutes.
11. Serve hot with buns, green salad, tomato sauce, etc.

NUTRITION: Calories 439.12 Calories from Fat 148.97 Total Fat 17.48g Saturated Fat 1.71g

56. Powerful Spinach and Mustard Leaves Puree

Preparation Time: 10-30 Minutes

Cooking Time: 50 Minutes
Servings: 4
INGREDIENTS:

- 2 Tbsp almond butter
- One onion finely diced
- 2 Tbsp minced garlic
- 1 tsp salt and black pepper (or to taste)
- 1 lb. mustard leaves cleaned rinsed
- 1 lb. frozen spinach thawed
- 1 tsp coriander
- 1 tsp ground cumin
- 1/2 cup almond milk

DIRECTIONS:

1. Press the SAUTÉ button on your Instant Pot and heat the almond butter.
2. Sauté onion, garlic, and a pinch of salt for 2-3 minutes; stir occasionally.
3. Add spinach and the mustard greens and stir for a minute or two.
4. Season with the salt and pepper, coriander, and cumin; give a good stir.
5. Lock lid into place and set on the MANUAL setting for 15 minutes.
6. Use Quick Release - turn the valve from sealing to venting to release the pressure.
7. Move mixture to a blender, add almond milk and blend until smooth.
8. Taste and adjust seasonings.
9. Serve.

NUTRITION: Calories 180.53 Calories from Fat 82.69 Total Fat 10g Saturated Fat 0.65g

57. Quinoa and Rice Stuffed Peppers (Oven-Baked)

Preparation Time: 10-30 Minutes
Cooking Time: 35 Minutes
Servings: 8
INGREDIENTS:

- 3/4 cup long-grain rice
- Eight bell peppers (any color)
- 2 Tbsp olive oil
- One onion finely diced
- Two cloves chopped garlic
- One can (11 oz) crushed tomatoes
- 1 tsp cumin
- 1 tsp coriander
- 4 Tbsp ground walnuts
- 2 cups cooked quinoa
- 4 Tbsp chopped parsley
- Salt and ground black pepper to taste

DIRECTIONS:

1. Preheat oven to 400 F/200 C.
2. Boil rice and drain in a colander.
3. Cut the top stem part of the pepper off, remove the remaining pith and seeds, rinse peppers.
4. Heat oil in a large frying skillet, and sauté onion and garlic until soft.
5. Add tomatoes, cumin, ground almonds, salt, pepper, and coriander; stir well and simmer for 2 minutes, stirring constantly.
6. Take away from the heat. Combine the rice, quinoa, and parsley; stir well.
7. Taste and adjust salt and pepper.
8. Fill the peppers with a mixture, and place peppers cut side-up in a baking dish, drizzle with little oil.
9. Bake for 15 minutes.
10. Serve warm.

NUTRITION: Calories 335.69 Calories from Fat 83.63 Total Fat 9.58g Saturated Fat 1.2g

58. Quinoa and Lentils with Crushed Tomato

Preparation Time: 10-30 Minutes
Cooking Time: 35 Minutes
Servings: 4
INGREDIENTS:

- 4 Tbsp olive oil
- One medium onion, diced
- Two garlic cloves, minced
- Salt and ground black pepper to taste
- One can (15 oz) tomatoes crushed
- 1 cup vegetable broth
- 1/2 cup quinoa, washed and drained
- 1 cup cooked lentils
- 1 tsp chili powder
- 1 tsp cumin

DIRECTIONS:

1. Heat oil in a pot and sauté the onion and garlic with the pinch of salt until soft.
2. Pour reserved tomatoes and vegetable broth, bring to boil, and stir well.
3. Stir in the quinoa, cover, and cook for 15 minutes; stir occasionally.
4. Add in lentils, chili powder, and cumin; cook for further 5 minutes.
5. Taste and adjust seasonings.
6. Serve immediately.
7. Keep refrigerated in a covered container for 4 - 5 days.

NUTRITION: Calories 397.45 Calories from Fat 138.18 Total Fat 15.61g Saturated Fat 2.14g

59. Silk Tofu Penne with Spinach

Preparation Time: 10-30 Minutes
Cooking Time: 25 Minutes
Servings: 4
INGREDIENTS:

- 1 lb. penne, uncooked
- 12 oz of frozen spinach, thawed
- 1 cup silken tofu mashed
- 1/2 cup soy milk (unsweetened)
- 1/2 cup vegetable broth
- 1 Tbsp white wine vinegar
- 1/2 tsp Italian seasoning
- Salt and ground pepper to taste

DIRECTIONS:

1. Cook penne pasta; rinse and drain in a colander.
2. Drain spinach well.
3. Place spinach with all remaining ingredients in a blender and beat until smooth.
4. Pour the spinach mixture over pasta.
5. Taste and adjust the salt and pepper.
6. Store pasta in a sealed container in the refrigerator for 3 to 5 days.

NUTRITION: Calories 492.8 Calories from Fat 27.06 Total Fat 3.07g, Saturated Fat 0.38g

60. Slow-Cooked Butter Beans, Okra and Potatoes Stew

Preparation Time: 10-30 Minutes
Cooking Time: 6 Hours and 5 Minutes
Servings: 6
INGREDIENTS:

- 2 cups frozen butter (lima) beans, thawed
- 1 cup frozen okra, thawed
- Two large russet potatoes cut into cubes
- One can (6 oz) whole-kernel corn, drained
- One large carrot sliced
- One green bell pepper finely chopped
- 1 cup green peas
- 1/2 cup chopped celery
- One medium onion finely chopped
- 2 cups vegetable broth
- Two cans (6 oz) tomato sauce
- 1 cup of water
- 1/2 tsp salt and newly ground black pepper

DIRECTIONS:
1. Combine the real ingredients in your Slow Cooker; give a good stir.
2. Cover and cook on HIGH for 5 to 6 hours.
3. Taste adjusts seasonings and serve hot.

NUTRITION: Calories 241.71 Calories from Fat 11.22 Total Fat 1.28g Saturated Fat 0.27g

61. Vegan Wrap with Apples and Spicy Hummus

Preparation Time: 10 Minutes
Cooking Time: 0 Minutes
Servings: 2
INGREDIENTS:
- One tortilla
- 6-7 tbsp Spicy Hummus (mix it with a few tbsp of salsa)
- Only some leaves of fresh spinach or romaine lettuce
- 1 tsp fresh lemon juice
- 1½ cups broccoli slaw
- ½ apple, sliced thin
- 4 tsp dairy-free plain unsweetened yogurt
- Salt and pepper

DIRECTIONS:
1. Mix the yogurt and the lemon juice with the broccoli slaw. Add the salt and a dash of pepper for taste. Mix well and set aside.
2. Lay the tortilla flat.
3. Spread the spicy hummus over the tortilla.
4. Lay the lettuce down on the hummus.
5. On one half, pile the broccoli slaw on the lettuce.
6. Place the apple slices on the slaw.

7. Fold the sides of the tortilla up, starting with the end that has the apple and the slaw. Roll tightly.
8. Cut it in half and serve.

NUTRITION: Calories: 205 Fat: 2 g Protein: 12 g Carbs: 32 g Fiber: 9g

62. Bell-Pepper Corn Wrapped in Tortilla

Preparation Time: 5 Minutes
Cooking Time: 15 Minutes
Servings: 4
INGREDIENTS:
- One small red bell pepper, chopped
- One small yellow onion, diced
- One tablespoon water
- Two cobs grilled corn kernels
- Four large tortillas
- Four pieces commercial vegan nuggets, chopped
- mixed greens for garnish

DIRECTIONS:
1. Preparing the Ingredients. Preheat the Instant Crisp Air Fryer to 400°F.
2. In a skillet heated over medium heat, water sautés the vegan nuggets and the onions, bell peppers, and corn kernels. Set aside.
3. Place filling inside the corn tortillas.
4. Air Frying. Lock the air fryer lid. Fold the tortillas and place inside the Instant Crisp Air Fryer and cook for 15 minutes until the tortilla wraps are crispy.
5. Serve with mixed greens on top.

NUTRITION: Calories: 548 Fat: 20.7g Protein: 46g

63. Rice and Veggie Bowl

Preparation Time: 5 Minutes
Cooking Time: 15 Minutes
Servings: 6
INGREDIENTS:
- 2 tbsp coconut oil
- 1 tsp ground cumin
- 1 tsp ground turmeric
- 1 tsp chili powder
- One red bell pepper, chopped
- 1 tsp tomato paste
- One bunch of broccolis, cut into bite-sized florets with short stems
- 1 tsp salt, to taste
- One large red onion, sliced

- Two garlic cloves, minced
- One head of cauliflower, sliced into bite-sized florets
- 2 cups cooked rice
- Newly ground black pepper to taste

DIRECTIONS:

1. Heat the coconut grease over medium-high heat in a large pan
2. Wait until the oil is hot, stir in the turmeric, cumin, chili powder, salt, and tomato paste.
3. Cook the content for 1 minute. Stir repeatedly until the spices are fragrant.
4. Add the garlic and onion. Sauté for 3 minutes or until the onions are softened.
5. Add the broccoli, cauliflower, and bell pepper. Cover the pot. Cook for 3 to 4 minutes and stir occasionally.
6. Add the cooked rice. Stir so it will combine well with the vegetables—Cook for 2 to 3 minutes. Stir until the rice is warmed through.
7. Check the seasoning. And make adjustments to taste if desired.
8. Lower the heat and cook on low for 2 to 3 more minutes so the flavors will meld.
9. Serve with freshly ground black pepper.

NUTRITION: Calories: 260 Fat: 9 g Protein: 9 g Carbs: 36 g Fiber: 5g

64. Zucchini Pasta Salad

Preparation Time: 4 Minutes
Cooking Time: 0 Minutes
Servings: 15
INGREDIENTS:

- Five tablespoons olive oil
- Two teaspoons Dijon mustard
- Three tablespoons red-wine vinegar
- One clove garlic, grated
- Two tablespoons fresh oregano, chopped
- One shallot, chopped
- ¼ teaspoon red pepper flakes
- 16 oz. zucchini noodles
- ¼ cup Kalamata olives pitted
- 3 cups cherry tomatoes, sliced in half
- ¾ cup Parmesan cheese shaved

DIRECTIONS:

1. Mix the olive oil, Dijon mustard, red wine vinegar, garlic, and oregano, shallot, and red pepper flakes in a bowl.
2. Stir in the zucchini noodles.
3. Sprinkle on top the olives, tomatoes, and Parmesan cheese.

NUTRITION: Calories 299 Fat 24.7 g Saturated fat 5.1 g Carbohydrates 11.6 g Fiber 2.8 g Protein 7 g

65. Egg Avocado Salad

Preparation Time: 10 Minutes
Cooking Time: 0 Minutes
Servings: 4
INGREDIENTS:

- One avocado
- Six hard-boiled eggs, peeled and chopped
- One tablespoon mayonnaise
- Two tablespoons freshly squeezed lemon juice
- ¼ cup celery, chopped
- Two tablespoons chives, chopped
- Salt and pepper to taste

DIRECTIONS:

1. Add the avocado to a large bowl.
2. Mash the avocado using a fork.
3. Stir in the egg and mash the eggs.
4. Add the mayo, lemon juice, celery, chives, salt, and pepper.
5. Chill in the refrigerator. Wait for at least 30 minutes before serving.

NUTRITION: Calories 224 Fat 18 g Saturated fat 3.9 g Carbohydrates 6.1 g Fiber 3.6 g Protein 10.6 g

66. Sautéed Cabbage

Preparation Time: 8 Minutes
Cooking Time: 12 Minutes
Servings: 8
INGREDIENTS:

- ¼ cup butter
- One onion, sliced thinly
- One head cabbage, sliced into wedges
- Salt and pepper to taste
- Crumbled crispy bacon bits

DIRECTIONS:

1. Add the butter to a pan over medium-high heat.
2. Cook the onion for 1 minute, stirring frequently.
3. Season with the salt and pepper.
4. Add the cabbage then stir it for 12 minutes.
5. Sprinkle with the crispy bacon bits.

NUTRITION: Calories 77 Fat 5.9 g Saturated fat 3.6 g Carbohydrates 6.1 g Fiber 2.4 g Protein 1.3 g

67. Cucumber Tomato Chopped Salad

Preparation Time: 15 Minutes
Cooking Time: 0 Minutes
Servings: 6
INGREDIENTS:

- ½ cup light mayonnaise
- One tablespoon lemon juice
- One tablespoon fresh dill, chopped
- One tablespoon chive, chopped
- ½ cup feta cheese, crumbled
- Salt and pepper to taste
- One red onion, chopped
- One cucumber, diced
- One radish, diced
- Three tomatoes, diced
- Chives, chopped

DIRECTIONS:

1. Combine the mayo, lemon juice, fresh dill, chives, feta cheese, salt, and pepper in a bowl.
2. Mix well.
3. Stir in the onion, cucumber, radish, and tomatoes.
4. Coat evenly.
5. Garnish with the chopped chives.

NUTRITION: Calories 187 Fat 16.7 g Saturated fat 4.1 g Carbohydrates 6.7 g Fiber 2 g Protein 3.3 g

68. Cauliflower Rice

Preparation Time: 5 Minutes
Cooking Time: 20 Minutes
Servings: 4
INGREDIENTS:

- Round 1:
- tsp. turmeric
- 1 C. diced carrot
- ½ C. diced onion
- 2 tbsp. low-sodium soy sauce
- ½ block of extra firm tofu
- Round 2:
- ½ C. frozen peas
- Two minced garlic cloves
- ½ C. chopped broccoli
- 1 tbsp. minced ginger

- 1 tbsp. rice vinegar
- 1 ½ tsp. toasted sesame oil
- 2 tbsp. reduced-sodium soy sauce
- 3 C. riced cauliflower

DIRECTIONS:
1. Preparing the Ingredients. Crush tofu in a large bowl and toss with all the Round one ingredient.
2. Air Frying. Lock the air fryer lid—Preheat the Instant Crisp Air Fryer to 370 degrees. Also, set the temperature to 370°F, set time to 10 minutes, and cook 10 minutes, making sure to shake once.
3. In another bowl, toss ingredients from Round 2 together.
4. Add Round 2 mixture to Instant Crisp Air Fryer and cook another 10 minutes to shake 5 minutes.
5. Enjoy!

NUTRITION: Calories: 67 Fat: 8g Protein: 3g Sugar: 0g

69. Stuffed Mushrooms

Preparation Time: 7 Minutes
Cooking Time: 8 Minutes
Servings: 12
INGREDIENTS:
- 2 Rashers Bacon, Diced
- ½ Onion, Diced
- ½ Bell Pepper, Diced
- 1 Small Carrot, Diced
- 24 Medium Size Mushrooms (Separate the caps & stalks)
- 1 cup Shredded Cheddar Plus Extra for the Top
- ½ cup Sour Cream

DIRECTIONS:
1. Preparing the Ingredients. Chop the mushrooms stalks finely and fry them up with the bacon, onion, pepper, and carrot at 350 ° for 8 minutes.
2. Also, check when the veggies are tender, stir in the sour cream & the cheese. Keep on the heat until the cheese has melted, and everything is mixed nicely.
3. Now grab the mushroom caps and heap a plop of filling on each one.
4. Place in the fryer basket and top with a little extra cheese.

NUTRITION: Calories: 285 Fat: 20.5g Protein: 8.6g

70. Zucchini Omelet

Preparation Time: 10 Minutes
Cooking Time: 10 Minutes
Servings: 2

INGREDIENTS:

- One teaspoon butter
- One zucchini, julienned
- Four eggs
- ¼ teaspoon fresh basil, chopped
- ¼ teaspoon red pepper flakes, crushed
- Salted and newly ground black pepper, to taste

DIRECTIONS:

1. Preparing the Ingredients. Preheat the Instant Crisp Air Fryer to 355 degrees F.
2. Melt butter on a medium heat using a skillet.
3. Add zucchini and cook for about 3-4 minutes.
4. In a bowl, add the eggs, basil, red pepper flakes, salt, and black pepper and beat well.
5. Add cooked zucchini and gently stir to combine.
6. Air Frying. Transfer the mixture into the Instant Crisp Air Fryer pan. Lock the air fryer lid.
7. Cook for about 10 minutes. Also, you may opt to wait until it is done completely.

NUTRITION: Calories: 285 Fat: 20.5g Protein: 8.6g

71. Crispy Roasted Broccoli

Preparation Time: 10 Minutes
Cooking Time: 8 Minutes
Servings: 2
INGREDIENTS:

- ¼ tsp. Masala
- ½ tsp. red chili powder
- ½ tsp. salt
- ¼ tsp. turmeric powder
- 1 tbsp. chickpea flour
- 2 tbsp. yogurt
- 1-pound broccoli

DIRECTIONS:

1. Preparing the Ingredients. Cut broccoli up into florets. Immerse in a bowl of water with two teaspoons of salt for at least half an hour to remove impurities.
2. Take out broccoli florets from water and let drain. Wipe down thoroughly.
3. Mix all other ingredients to create a marinade.
4. Toss broccoli florets in the marinade. Cover and chill 15-30 minutes.
5. Air Frying. Preheat the Instant Crisp Air Fryer to 390 degrees. Place marinated broccoli florets into the fryer, lock the air fryer lid, set the temperature to 350°F, and set time to 10 minutes. Florets will be crispy when done.

NUTRITION: Calories: 96 Fat: 1.3g Protein: 7g Sugar: 4.5g

72. Coconut Battered Cauliflower Bites

Preparation Time: 5 Minutes
Cooking Time: 20 Minutes
Servings: 4
INGREDIENTS:
- salt and pepper to taste
- One flax egg or one tablespoon flaxseed meal + 3 tablespoon water
- One small cauliflower, cut into florets
- One teaspoon mixed spice
- ½ teaspoon mustard powder
- Two tablespoons maple syrup
- One clove of garlic, minced
- Two tablespoons soy sauce
- 1/3 cup oats flour
- 1/3 cup plain flour
- 1/3 cup desiccated coconut

DIRECTIONS:
1. Preparing the Ingredients.
2. In a mixing bowl, mix oats, flour, and desiccated coconut. Season with salt and pepper to taste. Set aside.
3. In another bowl, place the flax egg and add a pinch of salt to taste. Set aside.
4. Season the cauliflower with mixed spice and mustard powder.
5. Dredge the florets in the flax egg first, then in the flour mixture.
6. Air Frying. Place inside the Instant Crisp Air Fryer, lock the air fryer lid, and cook at 400°F or 15 minutes.
7. Meanwhile, place the maple syrup, garlic, and soy sauce in a saucepan and heat over medium flame. Wait for it to boil and adjust the heat to low until the sauce thickens.
8. After 15 minutes, take out the florets from the Instant Crisp Air Fryer and place them in the saucepan.
9. Toss to coat the florets and place inside the Instant Crisp Air Fryer and cook for another 5 minutes.

NUTRITION: Calories: 154 Fat: 2.3g Protein: 4.69g

73. Buffalo Cauliflower

Preparation Time: 5 Minutes
Cooking Time: 15 Minutes
Servings: 2
INGREDIENTS:
- Cauliflower:
- 1 C. panko breadcrumbs
- 1 tsp. salt

- 4 C. cauliflower florets
- Buffalo Coating:
- ¼ C. Vegan Buffalo sauce
- ¼ C. melted vegan butter

DIRECTIONS:
1. Preparing the Ingredients. Melt butter in microwave and whisk in buffalo sauce.
2. Dip each cauliflower floret into buffalo mixture, ensuring it gets coated well. Holdover a bowl till floret is done dripping.
3. Mix breadcrumbs with salt.
4. Air Frying. Dredge dipped florets into breadcrumbs and place them into Instant Crisp Air Fryer. Lock the air fryer lid. Set temperature to 350°F and set time to 15 minutes. When slightly browned, they are ready to eat!
5. Serve with your favorite keto dipping sauce!

NUTRITION: Calories: 194 Fat: 17g Protein: 10g Sugar: 3

74. Simple Grilled Portobello Mushrooms

Preparation Time: 5 Minutes
Cooking Time: 8 Minutes
Servings: 4
INGREDIENTS:
- Three tablespoons low-sodium soy sauce
- One tablespoon grated ginger
- Three cloves garlic, peeled and minced
- Three tablespoons brown rice syrup (optional)
- Freshly ground black pepper, to taste
- Four large portobello mushrooms stemmed

DIRECTIONS:
1. Mix the soy sauce, ginger, garlic, brown rice syrup (if desired), and pepper in a small bowl and stir to combine.
2. Arrange the mushrooms on a baking dish, stem-side up. Drizzle the marinade over the mushrooms and let stand for 1 hour.
3. Preheat the grill to medium heat.
4. Drain the liquid from the mushrooms. Do not forget to reserve the marinade.
5. Grill the mushrooms until tender, brushing both sides of the mushrooms with the remaining marinade, about 4 minutes per side.
6. Serve on a plate and enjoy!

NUTRITION: Calories: 17 Fat: 0.1g Carbs: 2.3g Protein: 1.8g Fiber: 0.4g

75. Grilled Eggplant Slices

Preparation Time: 10 Minutes
Cooking Time: 8 to 10 Minutes

Servings: 4

INGREDIENTS:

- Three tablespoons balsamic vinegar
- Two tablespoons low-sodium soy sauce
- Juice of 1 lemon
- Freshly ground black pepper, to taste
- One large eggplant stemmed and cut into ¾-inch slices

DIRECTIONS:

1. Preheat the grill to medium heat.
2. In making the marinade:
3. Stir together the balsamic vinegar, soy sauce, lemon juice, and pepper in a small bowl.
4. Brush both sides of the eggplant slices with the prepared marinade.
5. Arrange the eggplant slices on the grill. Set it for 4 to 5 minutes per side, brushing the eggplant periodically with the remaining marinade.
6. Let the eggplant cool for 5 minutes and serve hot.

NUTRITION: Calories: 56 Fat: 0.3g Carbs: 11.3g Protein: 2.0g Fiber: 4.2g

76. Broccoli Stir-Fry with Sesame Seeds

Preparation Time: 10 Minutes

Cooking Time: 8 Minutes

Servings: 4

INGREDIENTS:

- Two tablespoons extra-virgin olive oil (optional)
- One tablespoon grated fresh ginger
- 4 cups broccoli florets
- ¼teaspoon sea salt (optional)
- Two garlic cloves, minced
- Two tablespoons toasted sesame seeds

DIRECTIONS:

1. Heat the olive oil (if desired) in a large nonstick skillet over medium-high heat until shimmering.
2. Fold in the ginger, broccoli, and sea salt (if desired) and stir-fry for 5 to 7 minutes, or until the broccoli is browned.
3. Cook the garlic until tender, about 30 seconds.
4. Sprinkle with the sesame seeds and serve warm.

NUTRITION: Calories: 135 Fat: 10.9g Carbs: 9.7g Protein: 4.1g Fiber: 3.3g

77. Bok Choy Stir-Fry

Preparation Time: 12 Minutes

Cooking Time: 10 to 13 Minutes

Servings: 4 to 6

INGREDIENTS:

- Two tablespoons coconut oil (optional)
- One large onion, finely diced
- Two teaspoons ground cumin
- 1-inch piece fresh ginger, grated
- One teaspoon ground turmeric
- ½ teaspoon salt (optional)
- 12 baby bok choy heads, ends trimmed and sliced lengthwise
- Water, as needed
- 3 cups cooked brown rice

DIRECTIONS:

1. Heat the coconut oil (if desired) in a large pan over medium heat.
2. Sauté with onion for 5 minutes until translucent.
3. Stir in the cumin, ginger, turmeric, and salt (if desired). Combine the bok choy and stir-fry for 5 to 8 minutes or until the bok choy is tender but still crisp.
4. Pour water 1 to 2 tablespoons at a time to keep from sticking to the pan.
5. Serve over the brown rice.

NUTRITION: Calories: 447 Fat: 8.9g Carbs: 75.6g Protein: 29.7g Fiber: 19.1g

78. **Stir-Fried Veggies with Miso and Sake**

Preparation Time: 10 Minutes
Cooking Time: 8-9 Minutes
Servings: 4
INGREDIENTS:

- ¼ cup mellow white miso
- ¼ cup sake
- ½ cup vegetable stock
- One large carrot, peeled, cut in half lengthwise, and then cut into half-moons on the diagonal
- One yellow, medium onion, peeled and thinly sliced
- One large head broccoli, cut into florets
- One medium red bell pepper, seeded and cut into ½-inch strips
- Water, as needed
- ½ pound (227 g) snow peas, trimmed
- Two cloves garlic, peeled and minced
- ½ cup chopped cilantro (optional)
- Sea salt, to taste (optional)
- Freshly ground black pepper, to taste

DIRECTIONS:

1. Stir together the miso, sake, and vegetable stock in a medium bowl. Set aside.
2. Heat a large skillet over high heat. Add the carrot, onion, broccoli, and red pepper and stir-fry for 4 to 5 minutes. Combine water, 1 to 2 tablespoons at a time, to prevent sticking.

3. Fold in the snow peas and stir-fry for an additional 4 minutes. Put the garlic and continue to cook for 30 seconds. Pour the miso mixture into the skillet and cook until the veggies are tender.
4. When it is ready, stir in the cilantro if desired. Sprinkle with salt (if desired) and pepper. Serve warm.

NUTRITION: Calories: 110 Fat: 1.6g Carbs: 18.1g Protein: 5.8g Fiber: 5.0g

79. Grilled AHLT

Preparation Time: 5 Minutes
Cooking Time: 10 Minutes
Servings: 1
INGREDIENTS:
- ¼ cup Classic Hummus
- Two slices whole-grain bread
- ¼ avocado, sliced
- ½ cup lettuce, chopped
- ½ tomato, sliced
- Pinch sea salt
- Pinch freshly ground black pepper
- One teaspoon olive oil, divided

DIRECTIONS:
1. On each slice of bread, you need to spread some hummus. Then layer the avocado, lettuce, and tomato on one slice, sprinkle with salt and pepper, and top with the other slice.
2. Heat a skillet over medium heat, and drizzle ½ teaspoon of the olive oil just before putting the sandwich in the skillet. Cook for 3 to 5 minutes, then lift the sandwich with a spatula, drizzle the remaining ½ teaspoon olive oil into the skillet, and flip the sandwich to grill the other side for 3 5 minutes. Press it down with the spatula to seal the vegetables inside.
3. Once done, remove from the skillet and slice in half to serve.

NUTRITION: Calories: 322 Total fat: 14g Carbs: 40g Fiber: 11g Protein: 12g

80. Loaded Black Bean Pizza

Preparation Time: 10 Minutes
Cooking Time: 10 Minutes
Servings: 2
INGREDIENTS:
- Two prebaked pizza crusts
- ½ cup Spicy Black Bean Dip
- One tomato, thinly sliced
- Pinch freshly ground black pepper
- One carrot, grated
- Pinch sea salt

- One red onion, thinly sliced
- One avocado, sliced

DIRECTIONS:

1. Preheat the oven to 400°F.
2. Lay the two crusts out on a large baking sheet. Spread half the Spicy Black Bean Dip on each pizza crust. Then layer on the tomato slices with a pinch pepper if you like.
3. Sprinkle the grated carrot with the sea salt and lightly massage it in with your hands. Spread the carrot on top of the tomato, and then add the onion.
4. Pop the pizzas in the oven for 10 to 20 minutes, or until they are done to your taste.
5. Top the cooked pizzas with sliced avocado and another sprinkle of pepper.

NUTRITION: Calories: 379 Total fat: 13g Carbs: 59g Fiber: 15g Protein: 13g

81. Beet and Berry Smoothie

Preparation Time: 5 Minutes
Cooking Time: 0 Minutes
Servings: 2
INGREDIENTS:

- 1 cup water, chilled
- Two tablespoons lemon juice
- Four teaspoons coconut oil
- Two tablespoons honey
- 4 cups mixed frozen strawberries and raspberries
- Two small red beets, peeled, sliced

DIRECTIONS:

1. 1 cup water, chilled
2. Two tablespoons lemon juice
3. Four teaspoons coconut oil
4. Two tablespoons honey
5. 4 cups mixed frozen strawberries and raspberries
6. Two small red beets, peeled, sliced

NUTRITION: Calories: 300 Cal Total Fat: 11 g Saturated Fat: 8 g Carbohydrates: 60 g Fiber: 10 g Sugars: 44 g Protein: 4 g.

82. Orange Resolution Smoothie

Preparation Time: 5 Minutes
Cooking Time: 0 Minutes
Servings: 2
INGREDIENTS:
- ½ cup of orange juice
- 1 cup Greek yogurt
- 1 cup frozen mango chunks
- Two bananas, peeled, frozen
- ½ cup miniature carrots
- 1 cup frozen peach slices
- Two tablespoons honey
- ½ cup pineapple pieces

DIRECTIONS:
1. Gather all the ingredients.
2. Plug in a high-powdered blender, and then add all the ingredients into it in the order mentioned in the ingredients list.
3. Pulse for 45 to 60 seconds or more depending on the blender, until well combined and smooth, and then distribute the smoothie between two glasses.
4. Serve straight away.

NUTRITION: Calories: 199 Cal Total Fat: 6 g Saturated Fat: 4.5 g Carbohydrates: 34 g Fiber: 3 g Sugars: 28 g Protein: 5 g

83. Spicy Carrot, Avocado, and Tomato Smoothie

Preparation Time: 5 Minutes
Cooking Time: 0 Minutes
Servings: 2
INGREDIENTS:
- 3/4 cup coconut water, unsweetened
- ½ a medium cucumber, unpeeled, chopped
- One medium tomato, deseeded, chopped
- One avocado, peeled, pitted
- 1 cup chopped romaine lettuce
- One medium carrot, peeled, diced
- One lime, peeled, halved
- One clove garlic, peeled
- 3/4 teaspoon sea salt
- 1/8 teaspoon cayenne pepper
- One tablespoon olive oil
- 1 cup of ice cubes

DIRECTIONS:

1. Gather all the ingredients.
2. Plug in a high-powdered blender, and then add all the ingredients into it in the order mentioned in the ingredients list.
3. Pulse for 45 to 60 seconds or more depending on the blender, until well combined and smooth, and then distribute the smoothie between two glasses.
4. Serve straight away.

NUTRITION: Calories: 244 Cal Total Fat: 17 g Saturated Fat: 2.6 g Carbohydrates: 19.2 g Fiber: 9.2 g Sugars: 7.1 g Protein: 3 g

84. Zucchini Bread Smoothie

Preparation Time: 5 Minutes
Cooking Time: 0 Minutes
Servings: 2
INGREDIENTS:

- 2 cups almond milk, unsweetened
- ½ cup baby spinach leaves, fresh, rinsed
- ½ cup rolled oats
- 2 cups chopped zucchini, fresh or frozen
- One teaspoon ground cinnamon
- One tablespoon maple syrup
- ¼ teaspoon ground nutmeg
- ¼ cup walnut halves
- 1 cup of ice cubes

DIRECTIONS:

1. Gather all the ingredients.
2. Plug in a high-powdered blender, and then add all the ingredients into it in the order mentioned in the ingredients list.
3. Pulse for 45 to 60 seconds or more depending on the blender, until well combined and smooth, and then distribute the smoothie between two glasses.
4. Serve straight away.

NUTRITION: Calories: 317 Cal Total Fat: 13 g Saturated Fat: 1 g Carbohydrates: 43 g Fiber: 11 g Sugars: 17 g Protein: 13 g

85. Cauliflower and Blueberry Smoothie

Preparation Time: 5 Minutes
Cooking Time: 0 Minutes
Servings: 2
INGREDIENTS:

- 1 cup Greek yogurt, unsweetened
- Two tablespoons peanut butter

- One ¼ cup cauliflower florets, frozen
- Two clementine's, peeled
- ½ cup spinach leaves, rinsed
- 1 cup blueberries, frozen

DIRECTIONS:
1. Gather all the ingredients.
2. Plug in a high-powdered blender, and then add all the ingredients into it in the order mentioned in the ingredients list.
3. Pulse for 45 to 60 seconds or more depending on the blender, until well combined and smooth, and then distribute the smoothie between two glasses.
4. Serve straight away.

NUTRITION: Calories: 323 Cal Total Fat: 10.6 g Saturated Fat: 3.2 g Carbohydrates: 35.8 g Fiber: 9.4 g Sugars: 26.8 g Protein: 19.9 g

86. Butternut Squash Smoothie

Preparation Time: 5 Minutes
Cooking Time: 0 Minutes
Servings: 2
INGREDIENTS:
- 2 cups almond milk, unsweetened
- ½ cup of water
- 1 cup butternut squash pieces, frozen
- Two bananas, peeled, frozen
- 1 cup raspberries, frozen
- Two tablespoons hemp seeds
- Two tablespoons chia seeds
- One teaspoon ground cinnamon
- 1/4 cup peanut butter

DIRECTIONS:
1. Gather all the ingredients.
2. Plug in a high-powdered blender, and then add all the ingredients into it in the order mentioned in the ingredients list.
3. Pulse for 45 to 60 seconds or more depending on the blender, until well combined and smooth, and then distribute the smoothie between two glasses.
4. Serve straight away.

NUTRITION: Calories: 520 Cal Total Fat: 26.1 g Saturated Fat: 4.4 g Carbohydrates: 56.2 g Fiber: 15.8 g Sugars: 22.8 g Protein: 14.1 g

87. Avocado and Kale Superfood Smoothie

Preparation Time: 5 Minutes
Cooking Time: 0 Minutes

Servings: 2

INGREDIENTS:

- 1 cup almond milk, unsweetened
- 1 cup blueberry yogurt
- Two bananas, peeled, frozen
- One avocado, peeled, pitted
- 2 cups kale, destemmed, rinsed

DIRECTIONS:

1. Gather all the ingredients.
2. Plug in a high-powdered blender, and then add all the ingredients into it in the order mentioned in the ingredients list.
3. Pulse for 45 to 60 seconds or more depending on the blender, until well combined and smooth, and then distribute the smoothie between two glasses.
4. Serve straight away.

NUTRITION: Calories: 441 Cal Total Fat: 18 g Saturated Fat: 2 g Carbohydrates: 66 g Fiber: 10 g Sugars: 36 g Protein: 11 g

88. Pineapple Celery Smoothie

Preparation Time: 5 Minutes
Cooking Time: 0 Minutes
Servings: 2
INGREDIENTS:

- ½ cup almond milk, unsweetened
- One pear, cored, chopped
- Three stalks celery, chopped
- One banana, peeled, frozen
- One teaspoon honey
- 1 cup pineapple pieces, cubed

DIRECTIONS:

1. Gather all the ingredients.
2. Plug in a high-powdered blender, and then add all the ingredients into it in the order mentioned in the ingredients list.
3. Pulse for 45 to 60 seconds or more depending on the blender, until well combined and smooth, and then distribute the smoothie between two glasses.
4. Serve straight away.

NUTRITION: Calories: 205 Cal Total Fat: 1.5 g Saturated Fat: 0.7 g Carbohydrates: 42.2 g Fiber: 5.7 g Sugars: 32.2 g Protein: 2.4 g

89. Mango and Cucumber Smoothie

Preparation Time: 5 Minutes
Cooking Time: 0 Minutes

Servings: 2

INGREDIENTS:

- 1 ½ cup coconut milk, unsweetened
- Four teaspoons lime juice
- 1 cup baby spinach leaves, fresh, rinsed
- 2 cup mango pieces, fresh or frozen
- Four mint leaves, rinsed
- 1 cup chopped cucumber, deseeded, peeled
- 1/4 teaspoon cayenne pepper
- 1 cup of ice cubes

DIRECTIONS:

1. Gather all the ingredients.
2. Plug in a high-powdered blender, and then add all the ingredients into it in the order mentioned in the ingredients list.
3. Pulse for 45 to 60 seconds or more depending on the blender, until well combined and smooth, and then distribute the smoothie between two glasses.
4. Serve straight away.

NUTRITION: Calories: 170 Cal Total Fat: 4.6 g Saturated Fat: 0.5 g Carbohydrates: 33.5 g Fiber: 6 g Sugars: 28.2 g Protein: 2.6 g

90. Melon, Kale, and Broccoli Smoothie

Preparation Time: 5 Minutes
Cooking Time: 0 Minutes
Servings: 2

INGREDIENTS:

- 2 cups coconut water, unsweetened
- 2/3 cup broccoli florets
- 2 cups honeydew melon pieces
- One lime, peeled, deseeded, halved
- ½ cup kale, destemmed, rinsed
- 2 Medjool dates pitted
- ½ cup mint leaves
- 1 cup of ice cubes

DIRECTIONS:

1. Gather all the ingredients.

2. Plug in a high-powdered blender, and then add all the ingredients into it in the order mentioned in the ingredients list.
3. Pulse for 45 to 60 seconds or more depending on the blender, until well combined and smooth, and then distribute the smoothie between two glasses.
4. Serve straight away.

NUTRITION: Calories: 220 Cal Total Fat: 1 g Saturated Fat: 0.6 g Carbohydrates: 46 g Fiber: 8.6 g Sugars: 39 g Protein: 5.4 g

91. Avocado and Cucumber Smoothie

Preparation Time: 5 Minutes
Cooking Time: 0 Minutes
Servings: 2
INGREDIENTS:
- 1 cup water, chilled
- One large cucumber, deseeded
- One avocado, cored, peeled

DIRECTIONS:
1. Gather all the ingredients.
2. Plug in a high-powdered blender, and then add all the ingredients into it in the order mentioned in the ingredients list.
3. Pulse for 45 to 60 seconds or more depending on the blender, until well combined and smooth, and then distribute the smoothie between two glasses.
4. Serve straight away.

NUTRITION: Calories: 141 Cal Total Fat: 9.8 g Saturated Fat: 1.5 g Carbohydrates: 10.2 g Fiber: 6.4 g Sugars: 2.7 g Protein: 1.7 g

92. Apple, Banana, and Collard Greens Smoothie

Preparation Time: 5 Minutes
Cooking Time: 0 Minutes
Servings: 2
INGREDIENTS:
- 1 cup water, chilled
- Two green apples, cored
- One large banana, peeled, frozen
- 1 ½ cup collard greens, frozen

DIRECTIONS:
1. Gather all the ingredients.
2. Plug in a high-powdered blender, and then add all the ingredients into it in the order mentioned in the ingredients list.
3. Pulse for 45 to 60 seconds or more depending on the blender, until well combined and smooth, and then distribute the smoothie between two glasses.
4. Serve straight away.

NUTRITION: Calories: 179 Cal Total Fat: 0.6 g Saturated Fat: 0.2 g Carbohydrates: 40 g Fiber: 7.7 g Sugars: 27.3 g Protein: 3.1 g

93. Broccoli and Orange Smoothie

Preparation Time: 5 Minutes
Cooking Time: 0 Minutes
Servings: 2
INGREDIENTS:

- 1 cup water, chilled
- Two broccoli heads
- One orange, peeled

DIRECTIONS:

1. Gather all the ingredients.
2. Plug in a high-powdered blender, and then add all the ingredients into it in the order mentioned in the ingredients list.
3. Pulse for 45 to 60 seconds or more depending on the blender, until well combined and smooth, and then distribute the smoothie between two glasses.
4. Serve straight away.

NUTRITION: Calories: 241 Cal Total Fat: 2.1 g Saturated Fat: 0.7 g Carbohydrates: 43.3 g Fiber: 17.4 g Sugars: 16.5 g Protein: 11.3 g

94. Sweet Kiwi and Mint Smoothie

Preparation Time: 5 Minutes
Cooking Time: 0 Minutes
Servings: 2
INGREDIENTS:

- 1 cup water, chilled
- Two kiwis, peeled
- One medium lemon, peeled
- ¼ cup mint leaves
- ¼ cup parsley leaves
- Two teaspoons honey

DIRECTIONS:

1. Gather all the ingredients.
2. Plug in a high-powdered blender, and then add all the ingredients into it in the order mentioned in the ingredients list.
3. Pulse for 45 to 60 seconds or more depending on the blender, until well combined and smooth, and then distribute the smoothie between two glasses.
4. Serve straight away.

NUTRITION: Calories: 81 Cal Total Fat: 0.5 g Saturated Fat: 0.1 g Carbohydrates: 17.1 g Fiber: 3.4 g Sugars: 13 g Protein: 1.2 g.

95. Cucumber, Celery, and Apple Smoothie

Preparation Time: 5 Minutes
Cooking Time: 0 Minutes
Servings: 2
INGREDIENTS:

- 1 cup water, chilled
- ½ lemon, juiced
- One large stalk of celery
- Two medium green apples, cored
- One large cucumber

DIRECTIONS:

1. Gather all the ingredients.
2. Plug in a high-powdered blender, and then add all the ingredients into it in the order mentioned in the ingredients list.
3. Pulse for 45 to 60 seconds or more depending on the blender, until well combined and smooth, and then distribute the smoothie between two glasses.
4. Serve straight away.

NUTRITION: Calories: 131 Cal Total Fat: 0.6 g Saturated Fat: 0.2 g Carbohydrates: 28.8 g Fiber: 6.7 g Sugars: 22.3 g Protein: 1.3 g

96. Veggie Cakes

Preparation Time: 30 Minutes
Cooking Time: 30 Minutes
Servings: 8
INGREDIENTS:

- Two teaspoons ginger, grated
- 1 cup yellow onion, chopped
- 1 cup mushrooms, minced
- 1 cup canned red lentils, drained
- ¼ cup veggie stock
- One sweet potato, chopped
- ¼ cup parsley, chopped
- ¼ cup hemp seeds
- One tablespoon curry powder
- ¼ cup cilantro, chopped
- A drizzle of olive oil
- 1 cup quick oats
- Two tablespoons rice flour

DIRECTIONS:

1. Warmth a pan with the oil on medium-high heat, add ginger, onion, and mushrooms, stir, and cook for 2-3 minutes.
2. Add lentils, potato, and stock, stir, cook for 5-6 minutes, take off heat, cool the whole mixture, and mash it with a fork.
3. Add parsley, cilantro, hemp, oats, curry powder, and rice flour, stir well and shape medium cakes out of this mix.
4. Place veggie cakes in your air fryer's basket and cook at 3750 F for 10 minutes, flipping them halfway.
5. Serve them as an appetizer.
6. Enjoy!

NUTRITION: Calories: 212 Fat: 4 grams Net Carbs: 8 grams Protein: 10 grams

97. Cinnamon Coconut Chips

Preparation Time: 7 Minutes
Cooking Time: 25 Minutes
Servings: 2
INGREDIENTS:
- ¼ cup COCONUT chips, unsweetened
- ¼ teaspoon of sea salt
- ¼ cup cinnamon

DIRECTIONS:
1. Add cinnamon and salt in a mixing bowl and set aside. Heat a pan over medium heat for 2 minutes.
2. Place the coconut chips in the hot pan and stir until coconut chips crisp and lightly brown.
3. Toss toasted coconut chips with cinnamon and salt.
4. Serve and enjoy!

NUTRITION: Calories: 228 Fat: 21 grams Net Carbs: 7.8 grams Protein: 1.9 grams

98. Peach Cobbler

Preparation Time: 20 Minutes
Cooking Time: 4 hours
Servings: 4
INGREDIENTS:
- 4 cups peaches, peeled and sliced
- ¼ cup of coconut sugar
- ½ teaspoon cinnamon powder
- 1 ½ cups vegan sweet crackers, crushed
- ¼ cup stevia
- ¼ teaspoon nutmeg, ground
- ½ cup almond milk
- One teaspoon vanilla extract

- Cooking spray

DIRECTIONS:
1. In a bowl, mix peaches with coconut sugar and cinnamon and stir.
2. In a separate bowl, mix crackers with stevia, nutmeg, almond milk, and vanilla extract and stir.
3. Shower your slow cooker with cooking spray and spread peaches on the bottom.
4. Add crackers mix, spread, cover, and cook on Low for 4 hours.
5. Divide cobbler between plates and serve.
6. Enjoy!

NUTRITION: Calories: 212 Fat: 4 grams Net Carbs: 7 grams Protein: 3 grams

99. Chocolate Brownies

Preparation Time: 10 Minutes
Cooking Time: 20 Minutes
Servings: 4
INGREDIENTS:
- Two tablespoons cocoa powder
- One scoop protein powder
- 1 cup bananas, over-ripe
- ½ cup almond butter, melted

DIRECTIONS:
1. Preheat the oven to 3500 F.
2. Spray the brownie pan with cooking spray.
3. Add the real ingredients in your blender and blend until smooth.
4. Pour the batter into the prepared pan.
5. Put in the oven for 20 minutes.
6. Serve and enjoy!

NUTRITION: Calories: 82 Fat: 2.1 grams Net Carbs: 11.4 grams Protein: 6.9 grams

100. The Keto Lovers "Magical" Grain-Free Granola

Preparation Time: 30 Minutes
Cooking Time: 1 Hour and 15 Minutes
Servings:
INGREDIENTS:
- ½ cup of raw sunflower seeds
- ½ cup of raw hemp hearts
- ½ cup of flaxseeds
- ¼ cup of chia seeds
- Two tablespoons of Psyllium Husk powder
- One tablespoon of cinnamon
- Stevia
- ½ teaspoon of baking powder

- ½ teaspoon of salt
- 1 cup of water

DIRECTIONS:

1. Preheat your oven to 3000 F. Make sure to line a baking page with a parchment piece.
2. Take your food processor and grind all the seeds.
3. Add the dry ingredients and mix well.
4. Stir in water until fully incorporated.
5. Let the mixture sit for a while. Wait until it thickens up.
6. Spread the mixture evenly-giving a thickness of about ¼ inch.
7. Bake for 45 minutes.
8. Break apart the granola and keep baking for another 30 minutes until the pieces are crunchy.
9. Remove and allow them to cool.
10. Enjoy!

NUTRITION: Calories: 292 Fat: 25 grams Net Carbs: 12 grams Protein: 8 grams

101. Keto Ice Cream

Preparation Time: 10 Minutes
Cooking Time: 3-4 Hours to Freeze
Servings: 4-5
INGREDIENTS:

- 1 ½ teaspoon of natural vanilla extract
- 1/8 teaspoon of salt
- 1/3 cup of erythritol
- 2 cups of artificial coconut milk, full fat

DIRECTIONS:

1. Stir together the vanilla extract, salt, sweetener, and milk.
2. If you do not come up with an ice cream machine, freeze the mixture in ice cube trays, then use a high-speed blender to blend the frozen cubes or thaw them enough to meld in a regular blender or food processor.
3. If you have an ice cream machine, just blend according to the manufacturer's directions.
4. Eat as it is or freeze for a firmer texture.

NUTRITION: Calories: 184 Fat: 19.1 grams Net Carbs: 4.4 grams Protein: 1.8 grams

102. Apple Mix

Preparation Time: 10 Minutes
Cooking Time: 4 Hours
Servings: 6
INGREDIENTS:

- Six apples, cored, peeled, and sliced
- 1½ cups almond flour
- Cooking spray

- 1 cup of coconut sugar
- One tablespoon cinnamon powder
- ¾ cup cashew butter, melted

DIRECTIONS:
1. Add apple slices to your slow cooker after you have greased it with cooking spray.
2. Add flour, sugar, cinnamon, and coconut butter, stir gently, cover, cook on High for 4 hours, divide into bowls and serve cold.
3. Enjoy!

NUTRITION: Calories: 200 Fat: 5 grams Net Carbs: 8 grams Protein: 4 grams

103. Almond Butter Fudge

Preparation Time: 17 Minutes
Cooking Time: 2-3 Hours to Freeze
Servings: 8
INGREDIENTS:
- 2 ½ tablespoons coconut oil
- 2 ½ tablespoons honey
- ½ cup almond butter

DIRECTIONS:
1. In a saucepan, pour almond butter then add coconut oil warm for 2 minutes or until melted.
2. Add honey and stir.
3. Pour the mixture into a candy container and store it in the fridge until set.
4. Serve and enjoy!

NUTRITION: Calories: 63 Net Carbs: 5.6 grams Protein: 0.2 grams

104. The Vegan Pumpkin Spicy Fat Bombs

Preparation Time: 20 Minutes
Cooking Time: 1 Hour and 20 Minutes
Servings: 12
INGREDIENTS:
- ¾ cup of pumpkin puree
- ¼ cup of hemp seeds
- ½ cup of coconut oil
- Two teaspoons of pumpkin pie spice
- One teaspoon of vanilla extract
- Liquid Stevia

DIRECTIONS:
1. Take a blender and add together all the ingredients.
2. Blend them well and portion the mixture out into silicon molds.
3. Allow them to chill and enjoy!

NUTRITION: Calories: 103 Fat: 10 grams Net Carbs: 2 grams Protein: 1 gram

105. Orange Cake

Preparation Time: 25 Minutes
Cooking Time: 5 Hours and 10 Minutes
Servings: 4
INGREDIENTS:
- Cooking spray
- One teaspoon baking powder
- 1 cup almond flour
- 1 cup of coconut sugar
- ½ teaspoon cinnamon powder
- Three tablespoons coconut oil, melted
- ½ cup almond milk
- ½ cup pecans, chopped
- ¾ cup of water
- ½ cup raisins
- ½ cup orange peel, grated
- ¾ cup of orange juice

DIRECTIONS:
1. In a bowl, mix flour with half of the sugar, baking powder, cinnamon, two tablespoons oil, milk, pecans, and raisins, stir and pour this in your slow cooker after you have sprayed it with cooking spray.
2. Warm a small pan over medium heat. Add water, orange juice, orange peel, the rest of the oil, and the remainder of the sugar, stir, bring to a boil, pour over the blend in the slow cooker, cover, and cook on Low for 5 hours.
3. Divide into dessert bowls and serve cold.
4. Enjoy!

NUTRITION: Calories: 182 Fat: 3 grams Net Carbs: 4 grams Protein: 3 grams

106. Chia Raspberry Pudding

Preparation Time: 10 Minutes
Cooking Time: 3 Hours
Servings: 2
INGREDIENTS:
- Four tablespoons chia seeds
- ½ cup raspberries
- 1 cup of coconut milk

DIRECTIONS:
1. Add the raspberry and coconut milk into your blender and blend until smooth.
2. Pour the mixture into a mason jar.
3. Add chia seeds and stir.
4. Cap jar and shake.

5. Set in the fridge for 3 hours.
6. Serve and enjoy!

NUTRITION: Calories: 408 Fat: 38.8 grams Net Carbs: 22.3 grams Protein: 9.1 grams

107. Pumpkin Cake

Preparation Time: 20 Minutes
Cooking Time: 2 Hours and 10 Minutes
Servings: 10
INGREDIENTS:
- 1 ½ teaspoons baking powder
- Cooking spray
- 1 cup pumpkin puree
- 2 cups almond flour
- ½ teaspoon baking soda
- 1 ½ teaspoons cinnamon, ground
- ¼ teaspoon ginger, ground
- One tablespoon coconut oil, melted
- One tablespoon flaxseed mixed with two tablespoons water
- One tablespoon vanilla extract
- 1/3 cup maple syrup
- One teaspoon lemon juice

DIRECTIONS:
1. In a bowl, flour with baking powder, baking soda, cinnamon, and ginger, then stir.
2. Add flaxseed, coconut oil, vanilla, pumpkin puree, maple syrup, and lemon juice, stir and pour in your slow cooker after spraying it with cooking spray parchment paper.
3. Cover Up pot and cook on Low for 2 hours and 20 minutes.
4. Leave the cake to cool down, slice, and serve.
5. Enjoy!

NUTRITION: Calories: 182 Fat: 3 grams Net Carbs: 3 grams Protein: 1 gram

108. Banana Bread

Preparation Time: 10 Minutes
Cooking Time: 50 Minutes
Servings: 6 to 8
INGREDIENTS:
- 1½ cups flour
- One teaspoon baking soda
- One teaspoon baking powder
- ¼ cup brown sugar
- ½ teaspoon salt

- ½ cup rolled oats
- Three large ripe bananas
- Two tablespoons ground flaxseed
- 1/3 cup unsweetened soy milk
- 1/3 cup vegetable oil
- Two tablespoon maple syrup
- One tablespoon vanilla extract
- 1 cup mini dairy-free chocolate chips, divided

DIRECTIONS:

1. Preheat the oven to 350°F. Fat a loaf pan or line with parchment paper covering all four sides.
2. In a large bowl, combine the flour, baking soda, baking powder, brown sugar, salt, and rolled oats. Set aside.
3. Mash the bananas until almost no chunks remain. Add the flaxseed, milk, oil, maple syrup, and vanilla extract. Stir to combine.
4. Steadily pour down the wet ingredients into the dry materials and stir until just combined. Stir in ½ cup of the mini chocolate chips.
5. Drench the cake batter into the greased or lined pan and spread it out evenly. Sprinkle the remaining chocolate chips on top in an even layer—Bake for 50 minutes. You may also wait until a toothpick incorporated in the center of the cake comes out clean.
6. Cool it for 10 minutes.
7. Move it to a wire rack to continue cooling.

NUTRITION: Calories: 420 Total fat: 19 g Carbs: 57 g Fiber: 5 g Protein: 7 g

109. Apple Crisp

Preparation Time: 10 Minutes
Cooking Time: 40 Minutes
Servings: 6
INGREDIENTS:

- ½ cup vegan butter
- Six large apples, diced large
- 1 cup dried cranberries
- Two tablespoons granulated sugar
- Two teaspoons ground cinnamon, divided
- ¼ teaspoon ground nutmeg
- ¼ teaspoon ground ginger
- Two teaspoons lemon juice
- 1 cup all-purpose flour
- 1 cup rolled oats
- 1 cup brown sugar
- ¼ teaspoon salt

DIRECTIONS:

1. Preheat the oven to 350°F. Gently grease an 8-inch square baking dish with butter or cooking spray.
2. Make the filling. In a large bowl, combine the apples, cranberries, granulated sugar, one teaspoon of cinnamon, the nutmeg, ginger, and lemon juice. Toss to coat. Move the apple mixture to the prepared baking dish.
3. Make the topping. In the same large bowl, now empty, combine the all-purpose flour, oats, brown sugar, and salt. Stir to combine. Add Up the butter and, using a pastry cutter (or two knives moving in a crisscross pattern), cut back the butter into the flour and oat mixture until the butter is small.
4. Spread the topping over the apples evenly, patting down slightly—Bake for 35 minutes or until golden and bubbly.

NUTRITION: Calories: 488 Total fat: 9 g Carbs: 101 g Fiber: 10 g Protein: 5 g Calcium: 50 mg Vitamin d: 0 mcg Vitamin b12: 0 mcg Iron: 2 mg Zinc: 1 mg

110. Secret Ingredient Chocolate Brownies

Preparation Time: 10 Minutes
Cooking Time: 35 Minutes
Servings: 6 to 8
INGREDIENTS:

- ¾ cup flour
- ¼ teaspoon baking soda
- ¼ teaspoon salt
- 1/3 cup vegan butter
- ¾ cup of sugar
- Two tablespoon water
- 1¼ cups semi-sweet or dark dairy-free chocolate chips
- Six tablespoons aquafaba, divided
- One teaspoon vanilla extract

DIRECTIONS:

1. Preheat the oven to 325°F. Line Up a 9-inch square baking pan with parchment or grease well.
2. In a large bowl, combine the flour, baking soda, and salt. Set aside.
3. In a medium saucepan, mix up the butter, sugar, and water. Bring to a boil, stirring occasionally. Reduce from heat and stir in the chocolate chips.
4. Whisk in 3 tablespoons of aquafaba until thoroughly combined. Add the vanilla extract and the remaining three tablespoons of aquafaba, and whisk until mixed.
5. Add the chocolate mixture into the flour mixture and stir until mixed. Pour down in an even layer into the prepared pan. Bake for 35 minutes until the top is set, but the brownie jiggles when slightly shaken. Allow cooling completely, 45 minutes to 1 hour, before removing and serving.

NUTRITION: Calories: 369 Total fat: 19 g Carbs: 48 g Fiber: 1 g Protein: 4 g Calcium: 1 mg Vitamin d: 0 mcg Vitamin b12: 0 mcg Iron: 1 mg Zinc: 0 mg

111. Chocolate Chip Pecan Cookies

Preparation Time: 10 Minutes
Cooking Time: 16 Minutes
Servings: 30 Small Cookies
INGREDIENTS:

- ¾ cup pecan halves, toasted
- 1 cup vegan butter
- ½ teaspoon salt
- ½ cup powdered sugar
- Two teaspoons vanilla extract
- 2 cups all-purpose flour
- 1 cup mini dairy-free chocolate chips

DIRECTIONS:

1. Preheat the oven to 350°F. Line a large rimmed baking page with parchment paper.
2. In a small skillet over medium heat, toast the pecans until warm and fragrant, about 2 minutes. Remove from the pan. Once these are cool, chop them into small pieces.
3. Make use of an electric hand mixer or a stand mixer fitted with a paddle attachment, combine the butter, salt, and powdered sugar, and cream together on high speed for 3 to 4 minutes, until light and fluffy. Add the vanilla extract and beat for 1 minute.
4. Turn the mixer on low and slowly add the flour, ½ cup at a time, until a dough form. Combine the chocolate chips and pecans and mix until just incorporated.
5. Using your hands, a large spoon, or a 1-inch ice cream scoop, drop 1-inch balls of dough on the baking sheet, spread out 1 inch apart. Gently press down on the cookies to flatten them slightly.
6. Bake for 10 to 15 minutes. Wait until just yellow around the edges. Let it cool for 5 minutes.
7. Transfer them to a wire rack. Serve or store in an airtight container.

NUTRITION: Calories: 152 Total fat: 11 g Carbs: 13 g Fiber: 1 g Protein: 2 g Calcium: 2 mg Vitamin d: 0 mcg Vitamin b12: 0 mcg Iron: 0 mg Zinc: 0 mg

112. No-Bake Chocolate Coconut Energy Balls

Preparation Time: 15 Minutes
Cooking Time: 3 to 4 Hours for Chilling
Servings: 9 Energy Balls
INGREDIENTS:

- ¼ cup dry roasted or raw pumpkin seeds
- ¼ cup dry roasted or raw sunflower seeds
- ½ cup unsweetened shredded coconut
- Two tablespoons chia seeds
- ¼ teaspoon salt
- 1½ tablespoons Dutch-process cocoa powder
- ¼ cup rolled oats

- Two tablespoons coconut oil, melted
- Six pitted dates
- Two tablespoons all-natural almond butter

DIRECTIONS:
1. Mix the pumpkin seeds, sunflower seeds, coconut, chia seeds, salt, cocoa powder, and oats in a food processor. Pulse until the mix is coarsely crumbled.
2. Add the coconut oil, dates, and almond butter. Pulse until the mixture is fused and sticks together when squeezed between your fingers.
3. Scoop out two tablespoons of the mix at a time and roll them into 1½-inch balls with your hands. Place them spaced apart on a freezer-safe plate and freeze for 15 minutes. Remove from the freezer and keep refrigerated in an airtight container for up to 4 days.

NUTRITION: Calories: 230 Total fat: 12 g Carbs: 27 g Fiber: 5 g Protein: 5 g

113. Blueberry Hand Pies

Preparation Time: 6 to 8 Minutes
Cooking Time: 20 Minutes Plus Chill Time
Servings: 6 to 8
INGREDIENTS:

- 3 cups all-purpose flour, plus extra for sifting work surface
- ½ teaspoon salt
- ¼ cup, plus two tablespoons granulated sugar, divided
- 1 cup vegan butter
- ½ cup of cold water
- 1 cup fresh blueberries
- Two teaspoons lemon zest
- Two teaspoons lemon juice
- ¼ teaspoon ground cinnamon
- One teaspoon cornstarch
- ¼ cup unsweetened soy milk
- Coarse sugar, for sprinkling

DIRECTIONS:
1. Preheat the oven to 375°F. Set aside.
2. In a large bowl, merge the flour, salt, two tablespoons of granulated sugar, and vegan butter. Using a pastry cutter or two knives moving in a crisscross pattern, cut the butter into the other ingredients until the butter is small peas.
3. Add the cold water and knead to form a dough. Tear the dough in half and wrap the halves separately in plastic wrap. Refrigerate for 15 minutes.
4. Make the blueberry filling. In a medium bowl, mix the blueberries, lemon zest, lemon juice, cinnamon, cornstarch, and the remaining ¼ cup of sugar.
5. Remove one half of the dough. On a floured side, roll out the dough to ¼- to ½-inch thickness. Turn a 5-inch bowl upside down, and, using it as a guide, cut the dough into circles to make mini pie crusts. Reroll scrap dough to cut out more circles. Repeat with the second

half of the dough. You should come to an end up with 8 to 10 circles. Place the circles on the prepared sheet pan.

6. Spoon 1½ tablespoons of blueberry filling onto each circle, leaving a ¼-inch border and folding the circles in half to cover the filling, forming a half-moon shape. Use a fork to press the edges of the dough to seal the pies.

7. When all the pies are assembled, use a paring knife to score the pies by cutting three lines through the top crusts. Brush each pie with soy milk and sprinkle with coarse sugar. Bake for 20 minutes or until the filling is bubbly and the tops are golden. Let cool before serving.

NUTRITION: Calories: 416 Total fat: 23 g Carbs: 46 g Fiber: 5 g Protein: 6 g

114. Date Squares

Preparation Time: 20 Minutes
Cooking Time: 25 Minutes
Servings: 12
INGREDIENTS:

- Cooking spray, for greasing
- 1½ cups rolled oats
- 1½ cups all-purpose flour
- ¾ cup, plus 1/3 cup brown sugar, divided
- ½ teaspoon ground cinnamon
- ¼ teaspoon ground nutmeg
- One teaspoon baking soda
- ¼ teaspoon salt
- ¾ cup vegan butter
- 18 pitted dates
- One teaspoon lemon zest
- One teaspoon lemon juice
- 1 cup of water

DIRECTIONS:

1. Preheat the oven to 350°F. Lightly grease or shower an 8-inch square baking plate. Set aside.

2. Make the base and topping mixture. In a large bowl, blend the rolled oats, flour, ¾ cup of brown sugar, cinnamon, nutmeg, baking soda, and salt. Combine the butter and, using a pastry cutter or two knives working in a crisscross motion, cut the butter into the blend to form a crumbly dough. Press half of the dough into the prepared baking dish and set the remaining half aside.

3. To make a date filling, place a small saucepan over medium heat. Add the dates, the remaining 1/3 cup of sugar, the lemon zest, lemon juice, and water. Bring to a boil and cook for 7 to 10 minutes, until thickened.

4. When cooked, pour the date mixture over the dough base in the baking dish and top with the remaining crumb dough. Gently press down and spread evenly to cover all the filling. Bake for 25 minutes until lightly golden on top. Cool before serving. Store in an airtight container.

NUTRITION: Calories: 443 Total fat: 12 g Carbs: 81 g Fiber: 7 g Protein: 5 g

115. Homemade Chocolates with Coconut and Raisins

Preparation Time: 10 Minutes
Cooking Time: Chilling time
Servings: 20
INGREDIENTS:

- 1/2 cup cacao butter, melted
- 1/3 cup peanut butter
- 1/4 cup agave syrup
- A pinch of grated nutmeg
- A pinch of coarse salt
- 1/2 teaspoon vanilla extract
- 1 cup dried coconut, shredded
- 6 ounces dark chocolate, chopped
- 3 ounces raisins

DIRECTIONS:

1. Carefully combine all the ingredients, not including for the chocolate, in a mixing bowl.
2. Spoon the mixture into molds. Leave to set hard in a cool place.
3. Melt the dark chocolate in your microwave. Pour in the melted chocolate until the fillings are covered. Leave to set hard in a cool place.
4. Enjoy!

NUTRITION: Calories: 130 Fat: 9.1g Carbs: 12.1g Protein: 1.3g

21-DAY MEAL PLAN

DAY	BREAKFAST	LUNCH	DINNER	DESSERTS OR SNACKS
1	Delish Banana Porridge	Grilled Veggie Kabobs	Bell-Pepper Corn Wrapped in Tortilla	Strawberry Mango Shave Ice
2	Gluten-Free Breakfast Porridge	Vegetable Hash with White Beans	Zucchini Omelet and Cauliflower Rice	The Keto Lovers "Magical" Grain-Free Granola
3	Healthier Morning Oatmeal	Ratatouille	Potato Carrot Salad	Baked-Sesame Fries
4	Warming Breakfast Granola	Baingan Bharta (Indian Spiced Eggplant)	Buffalo Cauliflower	Veggie Cakes
5	Perfect Baked Oatmeal	Cauliflower and Potato Curry	Mediterranean Salad	Taco Pita Pizzas
6	Unique Quinoa Bread	Kale and Pinto Bean Enchilada Casserole	Crispy Roasted Broccoli	Cinnamon Coconut Chips
7	Weight-Loss Chia Pudding	Pistachio Crusted Tofu	High Protein Salad	Peach Cobbler
8	Favorite Banana Bread	Potato and Zucchini Casserole	Coconut Battered Cauliflower Bites	Vegan Fudge Revel Bars
9	Inspiring Blueberry Muffins	Instant Savory Gigante Beans	Zucchini Pasta Salad	Keto Ice Cream
10	Morning-Glory Muffins	Broccoli Casserole with Beans and Walnuts	Grilled Eggplant Slices	Chocolate Brownies
11	Hot Fruity Breakfast Cereal	Instant Turmeric Risotto	Bok Choy Stir-Fry	Apple Mix
12	Energy Boosting Oatmeal	Nettle Soup with Rice	Egg Avocado Salad	Almond Butter Fudge
13	Nutritious Overnight Muesli	Okra with Grated Tomatoes (Slow Cooker)	Stir-Fried Veggies with Miso and Sake	The Vegan Pumpkin Spicy Fat Bombs
14	Egg-Free Tofu Scramble	Oven-Baked Smoked Lentil	Arugula Salad	Orange Cake

			Burgers		
15	Fluffy Tomato Vegan Omelet	Powerful Spinach and Mustard Leaves Puree	Grilled AHLT		Chia Raspberry Pudding
16	Best-Ever Oatmeal Muffins	Quinoa and Rice Stuffed Peppers (Oven-Baked)	Simple Grilled Portobello Mushrooms		Pumpkin Cake
17	Crust-Less Mushroom Quiches	Quinoa and Lentils with Crushed Tomato	Loaded Black Bean Pizza		Secret Ingredient Chocolate Brownies
18	Earthy Beans Salad	Silk Tofu Penne with Spinach	Stuffed Mushrooms		No-Bake Chocolate Coconut Energy Balls
19	Wholesome White and Red Bean and Apple Salad	Slow-Cooked Butter Beans, Okra and Potatoes Stew	Broccoli Stir-Fry with Sesame Seeds		Blueberry Hand Pies
20	Mediterranean Quinoa Salad	Grilled Cauliflower Steaks	Rice and Veggie Bowl		Date Squares
21	No-Bake Coconut Chia Macaroons	Sauteed Cabbage	Vegan Wrap with Apples and Spicy Hummus		Homemade Chocolates with Coconut and Raisins

CONCLUSION

Twenty-one days have passed since you started the Daniel Fast. Now that it is over, you may have dropped a few pounds, committed to eating healthier, gained more energy, your skin has cleared, you feel at peace with your inner beings, or maintained your weight for better health. How did the Daniel Fast help you? Did the fast succeed your expectation? Have you grown spiritually? Is your connection with God more vertically then horizontally?

So, let's recap on the benefits of the Daniel Fast. The Daniel Fast is a self-body fasting cleanser where we are eliminating certain foods for 21-Days. During this time, you usually pray for God to do things you want to see changed in your life and by His Grace it will be done. You may have prayed for better eating habits, healing, spiritual guidance, and intervention. Let me encourage you to continue to pray for these things throughout the year. Keep your ears open to hear His voice and your eyes open to see the move of His hands over your life. Give praises and acknowledge Him always.

I suggested changing your eating habits at the beginning of the book. If you prayed for eating habit changes, that is awesome. This is the time you need to consider a plan that will keep you healthy for the rest of your life just by eating the right foods, exercising, and cutting healthcare cost. I always tell people before making or considering any changes in diet, it's better that you to talk with your physician.

I hope that this book had helped you to make better eating habits when the fast was over. If so, great! You may have lost weight on this fast. You should consider a plan that will help you maintain your new weight. I always say, "You can't out run your fork." (If you haven't heard that saying before, it means you can't out exercise a bad diet).

When there is a change in your eating habit whether good or bad, your body function changes in how it eliminates bodily fluids. You may feel this is not important because it is a fast, but releasing bowels at least 2-3 times a day and urine that forms a pale yellow to clear indicates that you are hydrated. The body should consist of these healthy functions even if you are not on a fast. You must maintain proper function of your bodies organs when you are fasting too. Especially the liver and the kidneys. Drink 8 glasses or more water every day and eat the suggested foods that will produce the fiber needed for proper elimination of toxins. If you don't like plain water add a ½ squeezed lemon or drink infused water (Infused water with fruit for 12 to 24 hours for more enhanced flavor).

Eliminating your bowels is important during the fast. Constipation can be a problem. If you are not able to have a bowel movement on the fast, you should drink more water, as well as hot lemon water before and after meals, drink herbal decaffeinated or buy Mag 07 at your local Vitamin Shoppe. We are supposed to eliminate waste at least 2-3 times a day. However, if you drink the tea, drink plenty of water for complete flushing of the bowels.

Consider meal replacements with smoothies, it would be sufficient for balancing the body with your food intake. With smoothies you can include snacks and water. Incorporate a moderate cleanse fast: 2 smoothies, sensible meal, 3 snacks, and water or a full cleanse fast: 3 smoothies, 3 snacks, and water. You will still receive the vitamins and antioxidants you need to provide fueling energy throughout the day.

Thanks for your support. I wish that your success in this journey.